Lasers

Other Books in this Series

LASERS

Tools of Modern Technology

Ronald Brown

Doubleday Science Series
Doubleday & Company, Inc.
Garden City, New York, 1968

First published in the United States of America in 1968 by Doubleday & Company,
Inc., Garden City, New York, in association with Aldus Books Limited.
Library of Congress Catalog Card No. 68-18081
Copyright © Aldus Books Limited, London, 1968
Printed in Italy by Arnoldo Mondadori, Verona

Contents

Picture Credits

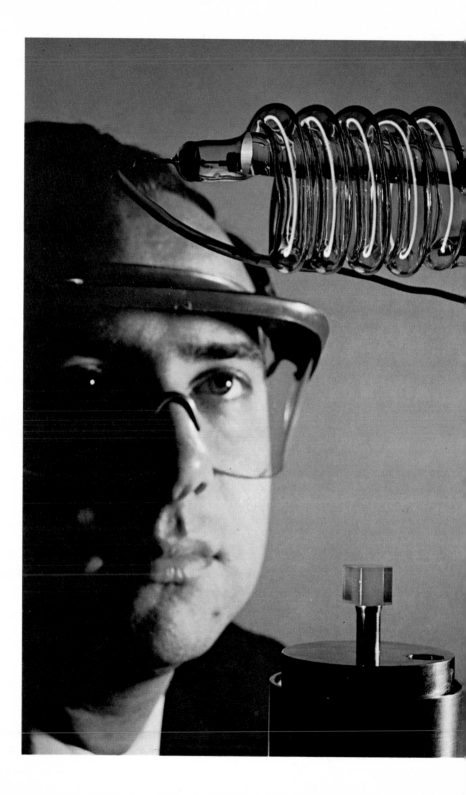

1 A New Kind of Light

The summer of 1960 saw the world's first demonstration of an entirely new source of light, which, on the one hand, is so concentrated and powerful that it can produce power densities billions of times as intense as those on the surface of the sun, and, on the other hand, can be controlled so precisely that surgeons use it to perform very delicate operations on the human eye. The beam from this new device can burn holes in steel plates and set carbon on fire, and it has many remarkable features apart from its power. It spreads out so little that if it were sent from the earth to the moon it would illuminate an area of the moon's surface only two miles in diameter. It is very "pure," all the light in it being of the same wavelength, and it is *coherent*, which means that all the light waves in the beam are exactly in phase with each other. These last two properties may not seem remarkable—they may not even mean much to most people—but to scientists and engineers they are very important for the technological benefits they bring.

Theodore H. Maiman, inventor of the ruby laser, with the main parts of the instrument. The glass helix at the top is a flashtube for supplying energy to the ruby crystal—the red cylinder with silvered ends passing down the middle of the helix.

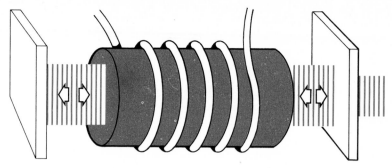

The main parts of a ruby laser. The heart of the instrument is the cylindrical ruby crystal, around which is the helical flashtube. Mirrors at each end reflect the light back and forth through the crystal and the laser beam emerges through the right-hand mirror, which is only partially silvered. In Maiman's original laser, the mirrors were coatings of silver on the end faces of the ruby crystal itself. A flowing-water system, not shown here, keeps the crystal cool.

The name of the new instrument is the *laser*, from the initials of Light Amplification by Stimulated Emission of Radiation— the process taking place inside it. In the few years since 1960 the laser has become well known as a weapon in the armory of James Bond's enemies and other film villains (or heroes). More important, it has given rise to a whole new technology. The tremendous expansion in its use is evident from the fact that at the end of 1964 only 200 eye operations had been carried out anywhere in the world with lasers, while 18 months later one American company could claim that 51,000 people had undergone eye surgery with the lasers it had produced.

The First Laser

The man who made the first laser was T. H. Maiman, a scientist working for the Hughes Aircraft Company in California. The photograph on page 8 shows him with the essential parts of his instrument: a flashtube and a cylindrical ruby crystal. The actual setup is shown diagrammatically on this page. The flash-tube is a device for producing very intense light. The ruby absorbs energy from the flashtube and in a very short time—a few thou-sandths of a second—reemits it, some in the form of light and the rest as heat. A small part of the light energy produced by the ruby consists of a red beam traveling parallel to its axis. It is reflected to and fro by the mirrors at either end, so that it passes through the crystal many times, and as it does so it is *amplified*—

that is, it picks up more energy from the ruby. This energy is also in the form of red light and travels along with the beam, so that the intensity is building up all the time. One of the two mirrors is only thinly silvered and therefore partially transparent, and allows a fraction of the light beam through. What emerges through this mirror is a laser beam. This, very simply, is what happens in the laser. In this chapter, we shall try to explain why it happens.

Since 1960 many different kinds of laser have been made. They do not all contain ruby, nor do they all use a flashtube. What they do have in common is an *active material* (e.g. the ruby) to convert some of the energy into laser light; a *pumping source* (e.g. the flashtube) to provide energy; and mirrors, one of which is semitransparent, to make the beam traverse the active material many times and so become greatly amplified.

Electromagnetic Waves

Everybody is familiar with waves in one form or another, but not everybody understands what is meant by a "light wave." Luckily there is another type of wave motion that is easier to understand than light waves, and more familiar, yet closely analogous to them. Suppose a man picks up one end of a long, heavy rope lying on a polished (and therefore frictionless) table. If he shakes his hand from side to side, waves travel along the rope. Although the waves travel, moving away from the man and toward the other end of the rope, none of the particles that make up the rope actually travels any distance in that direction; they only move to-and-fro about their original positions.

Light waves, like the waves on the rope, are a form of periodic "disturbance" moving away from a source. But the form the disturbance takes is much less tangible than the sideways displacement of a rope. The varying quantities in a light wave are electric and magnetic fields, and the lower part of the diagram on page 12 shows these fields in a light wave at one instant. We do not really need to draw both the magnetic and the electric field, since they are exactly in step with one another, and in future we shall represent a light wave by a simple curve like the one at the top of the same diagram. This curve could represent either the electric or the magnetic field; it does not matter which.

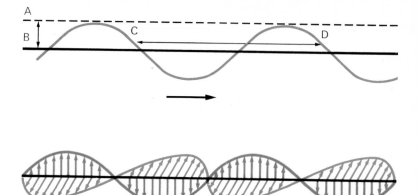

Top: wave motion. The wavelength is CD and the amplitude is AB, the height of the dotted line above the axis. Lower diagram: electromagnetic waves consist of electric and magnetic fields whose strengths vary in time and space. The magnitude and direction of these fields at one instant is shown by the arrows. The electric field (red) acts at right angles to the magnetic field (blue), which is perpendicular to the page.

Opposite: the electromagnetic spectrum. Light waves, indicated by the corresponding colors, form only a small part of this spectrum.

To a physicist, a wave is specified by four important quantities: its wavelength, frequency, velocity, and amplitude. The wavelength is the distance between any two successive crests (or two successive troughs, or any other two corresponding parts of the wave profile). The frequency is the number of waves passing a given point per second—which, in the case of the heavy rope, is the same as the frequency at which the man moves his hand. Frequency is usually expressed as so many *cycles per second*, or *cps*. The wave velocity is the velocity at which the wave profile moves forward, and it is not hard to see that it must be equal to the frequency multiplied by the wavelength. The fourth quantity, the amplitude, tells us the magnitude of the vibrations, and is defined as the height of a wave crest, or half the vertical distance from crest to trough. Wavelength and amplitude are shown in the diagram above.

Waves that consist of vibrating electric and magnetic fields are called *electromagnetic waves*, and light waves are by no means the only kind. Radio waves, infrared and ultraviolet rays, X rays and cosmic rays are also electromagnetic waves, the difference between them being their wavelengths. Radio waves are several meters, or

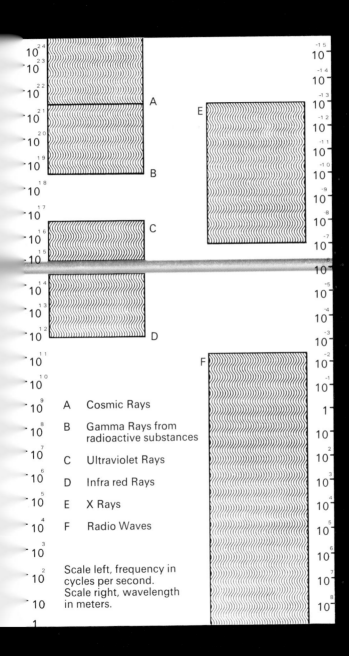

Scale left		Scale right
10^{24}	A	10^{-15}
10^{23}		10^{-14}
10^{22}		10^{-13}
10^{21}	B	10^{-12}
10^{20}		10^{-11}
10^{19}		10^{-10}
10^{18}		10^{-9}
10^{17}	C	10^{-8}
10^{16}		10^{-7}
10^{15}		10^{-6}
10^{14}		10^{-5}
10^{13}		10^{-4}
10^{12}	D	10^{-3}
10^{11}	F	10^{-2}
10^{10}		10^{-1}
10^{9}		1
10^{8}		10
10^{7}		10^{2}
10^{6}		10^{3}
10^{5}		10^{4}
10^{4}		10^{5}
10^{3}		10^{6}
10^{2}		10^{7}
10		10^{8}
1		

A   Cosmic Rays

B   Gamma Rays from
radioactive substances

C   Ultraviolet Rays

D   Infra red Rays

E   X Rays

F   Radio Waves

Scale left, frequency in
cycles per second.
Scale right, wavelength
in meters.

even hundreds of meters, in wavelength; X rays, on the other hand, have wavelengths of about one hundred-millionth of a centimeter and cosmic rays are about ten thousand times as short as these. Between these extremes is a group of waves that happen to be able to produce a sensation on the retina of the eye, and these are, of course, the light waves. They consist of all the electromagnetic waves between about 4000 and 7000 angstrom units in wavelength—an angstrom unit, denoted by the letter A, is 10^{-8} cm., or 0.00000001 cm. The 4000-A. waves, the shortest of the light waves, produce the sensation we know as seeing the color violet, the 7000-A. waves are those of red light, and the wavelengths in between correspond to the other colors of the visual spectrum. The invisible radiations immediately beyond the edges of the visible spectrum are the well-known ultraviolet and infrared waves. The complete spectrum of electromagnetic waves is shown on page 13.

One thing that all electromagnetic waves have in common is their velocity, which has the tremendous value of 3×10^{10} cm/sec (more familiarly, 186,000 miles per second). Because velocity = wavelength × frequency, as we have just seen, long wavelengths correspond to low frequencies and vice versa. Both the frequencies and the wavelengths are shown on the diagram on page 13. Notice that the scale on this diagram is not constant. At the bottom (where the longest radio waves are represented) a distance of about half a centimeter on the page represents the range from 1 to 10 cps, and a little further up, the same distance represents the range from 1000 to 10,000 cps. It is not possible to use the same scale all the way through. If we tried using the scale at the bottom of the diagram all the way through, we should need a page roughly 2000 million million kilometers high to contain the part representing the cosmic rays at the top! The kind of scale actually used, in which equal increments represent equal *multiples* of the frequency, is called a *logarithmic scale*.

Atoms and Light Waves

All light is emitted by atoms. When we switch an electric light on, the current supplies energy to the tungsten atoms in the filament, and these reemit the energy in the form of light—in more familiar language, the filament glows. Again, if we produce an electric discharge across some hydrogen gas in a glass tube, what is happening is that the hydrogen atoms are absorbing energy from the stream of electrons (cathode rays) and reemitting it as light and other electromagnetic waves.

There are rules governing the way in which an atom absorbs and reemits energy. Every atom has certain *energy levels* that represent its stable states. The levels for hydrogen, the simplest atom in existence, are shown on page 16. In this diagram the units of energy are *electron volts*: these are the normal units of energy used in atomic physics and they are, of course, minute by ordinary standards. For example, a calorie, which is the energy gained by a gram of water as its temperature goes up by one degree centigrade, is equal to about 30 million million million electron volts. The usual shorthand for electron volts is *ev*.

The lowest level of all in the diagram simply represents the normal state, or *ground state*, of the atom. The next one up is a little over 10 ev. above the ground state, and is called the *first excited state*. What this means is that a hydrogen atom cannot absorb an amount of energy less than 10 ev. If it is struck by a particle, such as an electron in a beam of cathode rays, whose energy is, say, 6 ev., the particle will simply be scattered without giving up its energy, because a hydrogen atom in its ground state cannot absorb 6 ev. If, on the other hand, it is struck by an electron of energy 10 ev. or more, it can absorb the 10 ev. and leave the balance of the energy with the electron, which travels on with reduced speed. The hydrogen atom is then left in its first excited state. For a little while it will stay there, then it will fall back to the ground state, emitting its 10 ev. as a "packet" of electromagnetic radiation.

Higher up still, above the first excited state, come the second, third, etc., excited states, corresponding to the larger amounts of energy that a hydrogen atom can absorb. An atom in an excited state may be compared to a compressed spring, since both are storehouses of energy, and an atom in its ground state is like a spring at its natural length. Whenever an atom jumps from a high energy level to a lower one, the energy it loses is given out as a packet of radiation.

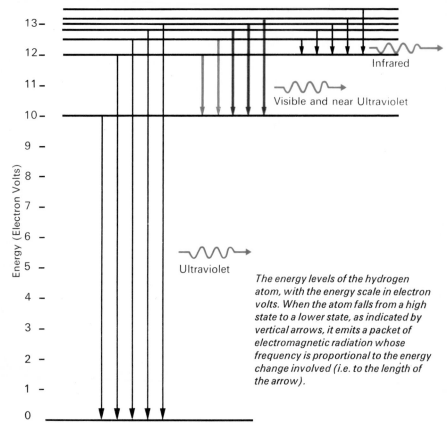

The energy levels of the hydrogen atom, with the energy scale in electron volts. When the atom falls from a high state to a lower state, as indicated by vertical arrows, it emits a packet of electromagnetic radiation whose frequency is proportional to the energy change involved (i.e. to the length of the arrow).

The hydrogen in a discharge tube consists of millions of atoms, many of them, at any one moment, in the ground state, others in excited states as the result of collisions with electrons. The excited atoms eventually fall to the ground state (either directly or via intermediate states), emitting electromagnetic waves at each step. At the same time other atoms are being excited up from the ground state by the discharge, so that the gas as a whole is continually taking energy from the electrons and giving it up, in the form of electromagnetic radiation, to the outside world. Much the same thing happens in a tungsten filament, although there the atoms of tungsten are raised to excited states by the energy of the electric current, not by a beam of cathode rays. Also, the energy levels of tungsten atoms do not, of course, have the same values as those of hydrogen. In fact, the energy-level diagram is characteristic of a particular type of atom, and is never the same for two different substances.

The last of the rules concerning atoms and electromagnetic waves is one telling us the frequency of the radiation produced by a particular atomic transition. This frequency is simply proportional to the energy of the packet. If the atom drops from a level of energy E_2 to a level of energy E_1 the frequency f of the radiation produced is given by:

$$E_2 - E_1 = h \times f$$

where h stands for a number well known to physicists, called *Planck's constant*, after the German physicist Max Planck. Once we know the frequency we can easily translate it into the corresponding wavelength (see the scales on either side of the electromagnetic spectrum on page 13).

The energy-level diagram for hydrogen (opposite) shows some of the possible transitions as vertical arrows; the longer the arrow, the higher the frequency of the emitted radiation. For instance, whenever a hydrogen atom falls from its first excited state at about 10 ev. to the ground state, it emits radiation of wavelength 1216 A., which is in the ultraviolet region of the

When the radiation from a hydrogen discharge lamp is passed through a prism and directed onto a photographic plate, the developed plate shows that only particular frequencies were present in the radiation. These correspond to the atomic transitions indicated in the diagram opposite.

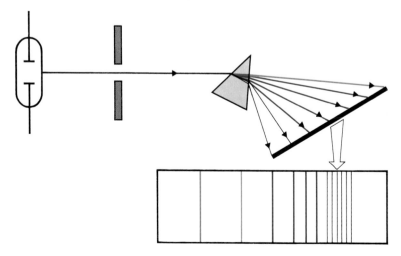

spectrum. Visible light of various wavelengths is produced when the atom descends from the second or higher excited states to the first excited state, whereas transitions ending on the second excited state produce radiation in the infrared region of the spectrum.

In case all this seems very abstract, the diagram on page 17 shows the experiment by which scientists can verify these frequencies. Light from the source—a hydrogen discharge tube—is split into its spectral components by being passed through a prism and is then allowed to fall onto a photographic plate. When developed, the plate shows a series of sharp lines separated by unexposed areas, proving that the light from the discharge tube contained only certain distinct frequencies. These frequencies can be deduced from the positions of the lines on the photographic plate, and their values may then be compared with those calculated from the energy levels on page 16. (Historically, of course, the calculation was done the other way round, and the energy levels of the hydrogen atom were found from the observed frequencies of the radiation.) The reason for using a photographic plate, and not just a white screen, to observe the lines is that the plate shows up some of the ultraviolet and infrared rays as well as the visible light.

We have said that radio waves and light waves are both forms of electromagnetic radiation, differing only in their wavelength, but anyone at all familiar with radio waves will, by now, have noticed another significant difference. Radio waves are produced by an oscillating dipole, such as a length of wire with a continuously alternating current flowing in it, and they are produced as long as the current goes on flowing, so that the output from the dipole is a long, smooth train of waves. Light, on the other hand, is produced in short bursts, each one called a *wave packet* or, in more modern terminology, a *photon*. A radio wave is a continuous flow of energy, whereas light consists of energy packets, each packet having energy equal to $h \times f$, where f is its frequency and h is Planck's constant. The light coming from an ordinary room lamp, although it seems to provide steady illumination, is really discontinuous, being made up of millions of these little energy packets.

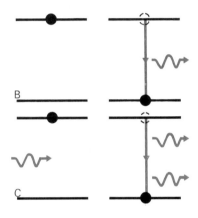

The radiation emitted by a particular atom is easily absorbed by another atom of the same species if the second atom happens to be in the right energy level, namely the terminal level of the transition that produced the radiation (diagram A).

A

Spontaneous emission (diagram B) occurs when an atom falls to a lower energy level of its own accord. The frequency produced is, of course, determined by the energy gap.

B

Stimulated emission (C) takes place if the atom is struck by a wave packet of precisely the same frequency as in diagram B before it has had time to emit spontaneously. Two wave packets emerge in phase with one another.

C

Stimulated Emission

So far, we have talked about atoms gaining their energy from an electric current or discharge. There are other possible ways, including one of special interest to us: an atom can be excited by absorbing a photon. This is only likely to happen, however, if the energy of the photon is just equal to the energy difference between two levels of the atom, the level it is actually in, and the level to which it is being excited. If the photon's frequency is too low, it does not have enough energy to raise the atom to the excited state; but if it is too high there is also little chance of absorption. The energies must match exactly. This absorption is clearly demonstrated by the fact that light emitted by (say) hot sodium vapor is easily absorbed by cooler sodium vapor. The cool vapor has more of its atoms in low energy levels than the hot vapor has, and the photons emitted by the hot vapor are, by definition, of just the right frequency to excite these atoms. This is shown on page 19, diagram A.

In 1917, Albert Einstein proved theoretically a fact that has come to have great technological significance. So far, we have referred to the fact that an atom in an excited state E_2 will eventually decay of its own accord to a state of lower energy E_1, emitting a photon of energy $E_2 - E_1$ as it does so. This process is called *spontaneous emission* and is illustrated in diagram B on page 19. What Einstein showed was that the event can be stimulated to occur before its natural time if the atom, in its excited state, is hit by an outside photon of the same energy, $E_2 - E_1$, as the photon to be emitted. After the event there will be two photons of the same energy leaving the spot, the original photon and the stimulated one. Einstein showed further that these two photons would leave together, *traveling in the same direction and exactly in phase with each other* (see diagram C on page 19).

It is easy to see that this process of *stimulated emission*, in which one photon comes in and two go out, contains the seed of a method for amplifying light waves. But until quite recently it did not arouse much interest because the chances of controlling the processes involved, which often occur in less than one hundred-millionth of a second, seemed very remote. Then, in 1954, three American scientists—James P. Gordon, H. J. Zeiger, and Charles H. Townes—put it to practical use for the first time. They succeeded in amplifying, not light, but microwaves. These are also electromagnetic waves, of wavelength from about 1 mm. up to 30 cm., produced by transitions between the energy levels of molecules, in the same way that light is produced by atoms. Microwaves are near the top of the block labeled F in the diagram on page 13. The new amplifying device was called the *maser*, standing for Microwave Amplification by Stimulated Emission of Radiation.

In 1958 Townes and the Canadian Arthur L. Schawlow wrote a paper in which they showed that it should be possible to use stimulated emission for amplifying light waves as well as microwaves, and two years later Maiman built the ruby laser that we have described. Because of its descent it was at first called an "optical maser," and it was only after three or four years that the name "laser" became widely accepted.

How the Ruby Laser Works

Let us now take a closer look at the ruby laser to understand its working in more detail. Ruby is a kind of impure aluminum oxide: a few aluminum atoms have been replaced by chromium atoms, which give ruby its characteristic color. The diagram at the top of page 22 shows some of the energy levels of these atoms. At the top is a shaded area, indicating that in this region many hundreds of energy levels are crowded together so closely that they form an *energy band*. Between the upper and lower limits of this band the chromium atom has, in effect, a continuous energy spectrum rather than the discrete type, consisting of well-separated levels, that we met earlier in connection with hydrogen. This is not because of any fundamental difference between a chromium atom and a hydrogen atom, but because energy bands like this are characteristic of atoms in solids and are not found in isolated atoms.

In addition to this band, and a little lower down, the ruby atom has an excited state at about 1.8 ev.—level 2 in the diagram—and the laser beam is produced by atoms falling from this level to the ground state. Under normal conditions many more chromium atoms are in the ground state than in the excited state. There is a constant traffic of atoms between states, each atom now absorbing energy, now emitting it; but the actual population of any state—the number of atoms in it at any time—remains about the same. In this condition the ruby cannot be used for amplification, because a photon produced by a chromium atom will almost certainly be absorbed by one of the many other chromium atoms, since most of these are in the ground state. For amplification by stimulated emission to occur, the photon must have a good chance of meeting another chromium atom in an excited state. What is needed is some way of producing a temporary *population inversion*, a situation in which many more atoms are in the excited state than in the ground state, as shown in the diagram at the bottom of page 22.

To produce such a population inversion we must pump energy

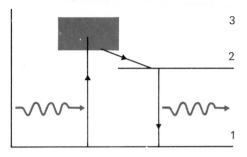

In a ruby laser, energy from the flash-tube raises the chromium ions to somewhere in the energy band shown as the shaded area (3). From here they drop to level 2, and the laser transition takes place between this level and the ground state, level 1. Strictly speaking, the various levels should be drawn one above the other, but some of them are often displaced sideways (as in this diagram) for the sake of clarity.

into the crystal to raise atoms from the lower state to the higher. This is the job of the flashtube (referring back to the diagram on page 10). The energy must be pumped in very quickly, because once an atom has been raised to the upper level it will only stay there for a short time—a few thousandths of a second—before falling back spontaneously to the ground state. If the energy is pumped in too slowly, the first atoms will be falling back before the others have been excited. Maiman used a powerful electronic flashtube connected to a large power supply, and discovered that there was a critical flash intensity needed to obtain a laser beam. If the intensity is below this level the decaying atoms produce only conventional, incoherent light.

There is another tricky point connected with the pumping process. The flashtube produces light of several wavelengths, but since only one particular wavelength—corresponding to the energy difference between levels 1 and 2—can excite atoms from the ground state to the excited state, it would appear that most of

Population inversion. Below: in the normal state of the crystal, most atoms or ions are in the ground state (open circles). Right: pumping energy in reverses this situation.

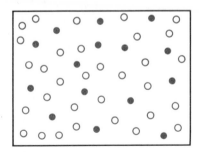

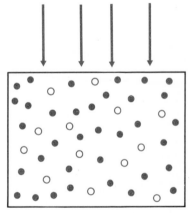

the energy of the flashtube is wasted. This is where the energy band comes in. Just because it is a band, and not a single level, it absorbs a whole range of wavelengths and is therefore much better than a single level at taking energy from the flashtube. In fact, the pumping process consists of raising chromium atoms to this band, and not directly to level 2. These atoms then fall a little in energy to level 2, losing energy as they do so, which appears as heat. In this way, level 2 can acquire a population greater than that of level 1.

Once the population has been inverted, lasing—as laser action has, rather improperly, come to be called—can begin. Sooner or later one of the excited chromium atoms will drop to the ground state, emitting a photon. If this photon strikes another excited atom, it will stimulate emission and two identical photons will emerge. If they strike yet another excited atom, further stimulated emission will occur, and in this way the strength of the light beam will quickly build up. If the beam happens to be traveling in a direction parallel to the axis of the tube, it will be reflected by the mirror at the end and, as it traverses the ruby crystal again, be amplified still more. Because of this to-and-fro reflection the light beam becomes very intense. It emerges from the half-silvered mirror as a laser beam, lasting about a half of one thousandth of a second. The complete process of inverting the population and building up the beam intensity is illustrated by the diagrams at the bottom of page 25.

The laser beam is red because the wavelength corresponding to an energy of 1.8 ev., the value of the energy gap between the two levels involved in the transition, is 6943 A., which is in the red part of the spectrum. It is a coincidence that the color of ruby is roughly the same as that of the beam. Ruby is red because of the two absorption bands in the energy-level diagram of the chromium atom—the one shown opposite and another one a little bit higher up. These bands absorb light strongly, as we have just seen, and the particular wavelengths absorbed correspond to green and yellow light (for the lower band) and ultraviolet light (for the other). When white light shines on ruby, therefore, only the red and blue components can pass through, and the mixture of these is responsible for the color of ruby.

Continuous-Wave Lasers

The ruby laser just described produces laser light in pulses. Often it is desirable to have a continuous laser beam rather than a series of pulses, in which case pumping energy must be put in continuously to maintain a population inversion. This can be done with ruby but it is difficult because large amounts of energy are dumped into the crystal when atoms fall from the absorption band to level 2 and the crystal becomes overheated.

Fortunately there is a way around this difficulty. Suppose we can find an active material other than ruby, with an energy-level diagram like the one on page 26, in which the laser action takes place between levels 3 and 2. After a photon has joined the laser beam, the atom that produced it stays in level 2 for a while and then decays spontaneously to level 1. To produce stimulated emission in this way we need only maintain a population inversion between levels 2 and 3, and it does not matter if the ground state (level 1) is more heavily populated than either of these two.

In any assembly of atoms—such as the hydrogen atoms in the discharge tube or the chromium atoms in ruby—the normal state of affairs is one in which population goes down as energy goes up. In other words, there are more atoms in the ground state than in any other, and the population of any state depends on how far above the ground state it is. Even a fairly small gap in energy will lead to a much lower population. In the *four-level*

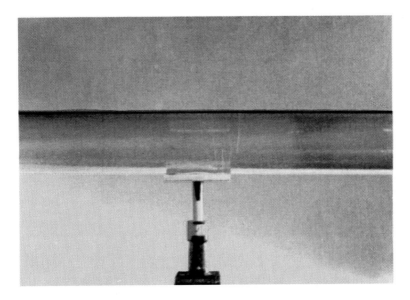

The ruby laser (opposite) produces radiation in an intense but very short pulse, lasting about one thousandth of a second. To view such a short pulse one must pass the beam through a smoke-filled tube (above).

Below: How a laser beam is produced. Upper diagram: pumping establishes a population inversion. Lower diagram: an atom becoming deexcited emits a wave packet toward one of the mirrors. The wave packet stimulates a second atom to emit, and this process is repeated as the light wave is reflected to and fro by the end mirrors. In this way the intensity of the beam builds up until it emerges from the half-silvered mirror on the right.

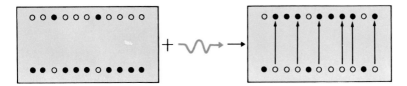

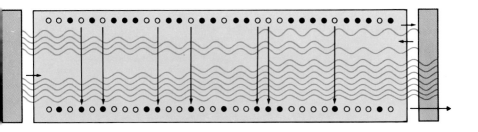

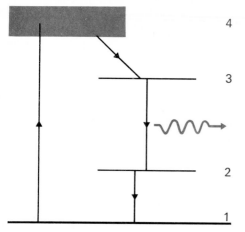

4

3 *A four-level laser system. Pumping energy raises atoms to the absorption band (4) and laser action occurs between levels 3 and 2. Because the terminal level (2) is not the ground state, it is relatively easy to produce a population inversion. Most four-level*

2 *systems, but not all, are used in continuously operating lasers.*

1

system shown on this page, both level 2 and level 3 have populations much lower than those of level 1. Level 2 is still, normally, more heavily populated than level 3, but the difference is not nearly as great as that between levels 1 and 2, and less energy is needed to produce and maintain a population inversion between them. Much less energy is dumped into the crystal, and it is much easier to operate the laser continuously, rather than in pulses. As we shall see in the next chapter, there are materials with suitable energy levels, and continuous-wave lasers are now very important. For the sake of accuracy, though, we should point out that not all four-level laser systems operate continuously, nor are all continuously operating lasers based on the use of active materials with four-level systems.

Why is Laser Light Unique?

The beam from a laser is superior to light from any conventional source in four respects: intensity, directionality, coherence and bandwidth. These characteristics are not all independent of one another, because directionality and bandwidth are really the lateral and longitudinal aspects, respectively, of coherence; but in terms of their practical consequences we may think of them separately, and talk about each in turn.

A pulse from a ruby laser, focused by a lens, can blast a hole in steel plate a third of a centimeter thick, yet it does not contain enough energy to boil an egg. There is no contradiction here: although the total energy in a pulse is not very great, it is very highly concentrated. The reason for this lies in the nature of the stimulated emission process. Each atom is synchronized to add its contribution to the laser beam at precisely the right moment, so that the new photon is in phase with the rest of the beam and the amplitude of the beam is increased as much as possible. The process is analogous to the generation of power in an automobile engine by explosions of fuel in four or more cylinders. Each cylinder is the equivalent of an individual atom in the sense that it contributes regular packets of energy to the total output of the engine. The timing of the explosions is carefully controlled so that each cylinder delivers its energy at precisely the right moment, when it will add to the power supplied by the other cylinders. If the timing is incorrect—as the result of the leads to the spark plugs being connected in the wrong order, for instance—some of the cylinders will deliver their packets of energy at times when they add very little to the total, or even when they oppose the energy being supplied by the other cylinders. Anyone who has driven a car in this condition will know the result: the total energy output is very small indeed.

In a conventional light source, such as a tungsten filament, the individual atoms produce their energy with random timing, like an automobile engine in which the firing of the cylinders is out of synchronism. An atom of tungsten is excited, decays spontaneously, emitting a photon, and waits to be reexcited. This may happen almost immediately, or it may take quite a long time. While it is waiting, other atoms are sending out photons in the same way. If the light thus produced is focused onto a steel plate, an irregular stream of photons will hit the plate one after another, and these photons will not all hit the steel at precisely the same spot but over an area defined by the image of the filament. In other words the energy is spread over too long a time and too great an area to produce much effect. With a laser beam, on the other hand, the photons combine to form a single, narrow beam of high amplitude, and several million of them hit a tiny area of the steel during the extremely short time for which the laser pulse lasts.

The laser beams used in eye operations are focused to spots only one tenth of a millimeter in diameter. The directionality of

A laser beam that damages one material may have little effect on another one. Here Arthur L. Schawlow, one of the first scientists to predict the existence of the laser, fires a toy ray gun converted for use with a laser beam. The beam bursts the inner balloon without harming the outer one, which was made of a substance that does not absorb light of the particular wavelength used.

the laser beam is a direct consequence of the mirrors at the ends of the optical cavity. A beam can easily start in some direction not parallel to the crystal axis, and it may trigger off photons from atoms in its path, but sooner or later it will pass out of the laser system altogether. This may happen before it has even reached either of the end mirrors, or it may happen after one or two reflections, but in any case it will not be amplified very much because it will not spend enough time in the crystal. Only when a beam starts off parallel to the crystal axis will the mirrors keep it inside the crystal for any length of time.

The third important characteristic of laser light is its coherence. This means that the different light waves in the beam are exactly in step with one another—or, to put it more scientifically, they have the same phase. The difference between coherent laser light and incoherent light of the kind emitted by a tungsten filament is shown in the diagram on the opposite page. Laser light is coherent simply because the process of stimulated emission always produces a photon that is in phase with the original light beam.

Coherence is important because only with coherent light is it possible to observe *interference effects*. These occur when two or more wave trains overlap and therefore interact. Interference effects can quite easily be produced and observed in waves on the surface of a liquid such as water, by the ripple-tank experiment shown at the bottom right-hand corner of page 30. A ripple tank is the apparatus used to study waves in liquids, and in this experiment there are two sources of waves, each of them a strip of metal with one end clamped and the other touching the water surface, which has been set vibrating. The waves are shown up by a special lighting arrangement. The photograph shows clearly that there are regions where the water surface is quite calm, indicating that the two sets of waves—one spreading out from each strip of metal—are opposing each other and canceling each other out. In other places the two are reinforcing each other, producing waves twice as high as either strip of metal would produce on its own. Where the water surface is calm, the disturbances produced by the two strips are exactly out of phase with each other; where the waves are highest they are exactly in phase.

Interference effects occur with light waves just as with water waves, but they are harder to show. The experiment analogous to the ripple-tank experiment would be to use two atoms in place of the two metal strips. Even if we could overcome the practical difficulties of doing such an experiment, and if we could observe the wave-patterns produced by such faint sources—which we could not—the experiment would not work, because atoms produce light in occasional bursts, whereas the metal strips each

Coherent and incoherent waves. With ordinary incoherent light (left), a line drawn at right angles to the direction of the beam intersects different waves at different points in their cycle, whereas the waves in a coherent light beam (right) are all in step with one another.

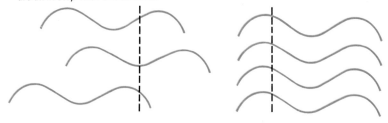

produce continuous streams of waves. The photons produced by the two atoms *could* interfere with one another, but only if both atoms happen to emit at the same time, or very nearly the same time, which would happen infrequently. Usually a photon emitted by one atom does not overlap one emitted by the other.

Using an atom as a source of light waves is rather like producing water waves not by a steadily vibrating strip of metal but by tossing an occasional pebble into the water.

In spite of these formidable difficulties interference effects in light were first observed, by the British physicist Thomas Young, as long ago as 1820. His experiment has become famous because, by showing that light rays interfere with one another, Young proved that light really can be thought of as a form of wave motion. We shall not describe the experiment here—not, at least, in its original form—but merely state that the first step is to control the source being used in the experiment by an aperture that excludes about 95 per cent of its light. In other words, the intensities of the coherent light waves produced by ordinary sources are always very small.

The laser is the first *intense* source of coherent light. The diagram at the top of page 32 shows how Young's experiment can be repeated, using a laser. A dark screen with two narrow parallel slits cut into it is placed up against the output end of a ruby laser, and a photographic plate receives the light emerging from the slits. Because of the nature of the laser beam, the light disturbance at one slit is exactly in phase with that at the other, so the two slits provide what the two atoms in our hypothetical experiment could not—two sources of light that are always in phase with one another.

At some points on the photographic plate the two rays of light (one from each slit) reinforce one another, and at others they oppose and cancel. The resulting photograph, shown at the right of the diagram, contains alternate light and dark regions, proving

The photographs at the top, and far left, show patterns produced by a gas laser. The patterns are due to the phenomenon of interference, illustrated for the case of water waves by the fourth photograph. Here, two vibrating strips of metal touching the water's surface generate waves that overlap and interfere with each other.

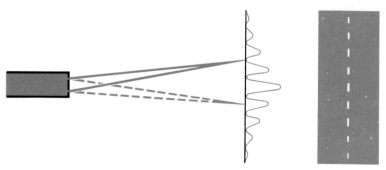

Producing an interference pattern with a laser. Light from both slits reaches the photographic plate, where the two sets of waves interfere with each other to give the alternate bright and dark regions shown on the right.

that interference has taken place. We shall see in Chapter 4 that interference has exciting technological applications that could not be exploited until the advent of the laser.

The last of the unique characteristics of laser light is its narrow bandwidth. All conventional light sources produce, simultaneously, light of more than one wavelength. A hydrogen lamp, for instance, produces a series of spectral "lines," as shown by the diagram on page 17. What is more, if we examine any one of these lines closely we find that it is not truly sharp but actually

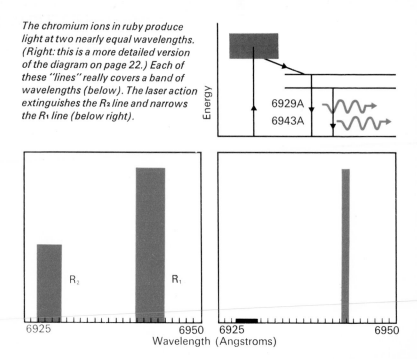

The chromium ions in ruby produce light at two nearly equal wavelengths. (Right: this is a more detailed version of the diagram on page 22.) Each of these "lines" really covers a band of wavelengths (below). The laser action extinguishes the R_2 line and narrows the R_1 line (below right).

Energy

6929A
6943A

R_2 R_1

6925   6950   6925   6950

Wavelength (Angstroms)

spreads over a band of wavelengths (hence the use of the word "bandwidth"). This is because the levels in hydrogen, shown on page 16, are themselves not quite sharp, but we have a certain fuzziness in their energy values.

Laser light—from certain kinds of laser, at any rate—is much sharper in its wavelength content than any other kind of light, and this too has important technological consequences, described in Chapter 3. The sharpness of laser light is, like its intensity and coherence, due to the special nature of the generating process. The energy-level diagram for a chromium atom in ruby is drawn again (opposite), this time in greater detail. The excited state at about 1.8 ev. is, in reality, two states of very nearly equal energy, so that a chromium atom can produce two closely spaced lines known as the R_1 and R_2 lines. They are called "lines" because that is how they would appear on a photographic plate in an experiment such as the one shown on page 17. Both these lines normally cover a fairly wide spread of wavelengths. It is the first of them that is involved when the ruby is used in a laser, and in that case it is very greatly narrowed. When stimulated emission

The coherence of laser light gives rise to these striking effects, observed in a laser laboratory, which are due to diffraction and interference.

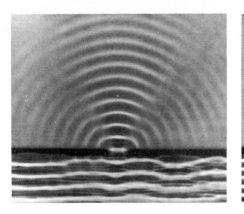

occurs, the incident photon stimulates another photon of the *same* wavelength much more readily than it will stimulate one of slightly different wavelength, so that the process selects one wavelength from the band of possible wavelengths and builds it up to the exclusion of others. The preferred wavelength is one for which the distance between the end mirrors is an exact number of half wavelengths. This is necessary if the wave pattern is to fit back into itself after a complete round trip. The result is shown in the diagram at the bottom of page 32, which compares the bandwidths in conventional and in laser emission.

Light Waves Around Corners

It is widely believed that light rays travel in straight lines. To demonstrate that this is not really true it is only necessary to close one eye and look at a fat pencil held up so as to block out the view of a naked electric light bulb. The edges of the pencil look bright because some light rays, bending round the pencil, are entering the eye, and for the same reason the shadow produced by the pencil on a screen is not completely dark.

This surprising fact, like many others about light waves, has an analogy in the behavior of water waves. The sequence of photographs above show some more ripple-tank experiments. The first picture shows clearly that when straight waves meet a barrier with a gap in it waves spread out on the other side of the gap, having bent as they went past the edges. This may not seem very surprising to anyone who has been at the seaside. What is more important is the way the behavior of these waves changes as the wavelength is reduced. The sequence of photographs show clearly that the smaller the wavelength, the less the waves spread

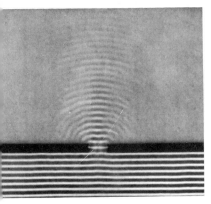

The phenomenon of diffraction is demonstrated in these experiments with water waves. When straight waves pass through an opening they spread out on the other side (far left). The extent of this spreading decreases as the wavelength goes down, as shown by the next two photographs. The first two pictures show interference occurring in certain directions. In all three photographs the waves are coming from below, and spreading out above, the barrier.

out, and more precise experiments indicate that what determines the degree of spread is not just the wavelength but the relative sizes of the wavelength and the gap.

In the last photograph of the sequence the waves hardly spread out at all. This is the behavior we normally associate with light rays, which form a sharp image of a hole when they pass through it; and this gives us a clue as to why light rays seem, in ordinary circumstances, to move in straight lines. Their wavelength is so short compared to any of the obstacles or gaps they usually meet that they bend very little. The bending is only significant when they squeeze through a very narrow gap or pass around a very thin obstacle.

As a matter of fact we have already taken the existence of this bending, or *diffraction*, for granted. In Young's experiment, illustrated on page 32, there would be no interference pattern produced on the photographic plate if light really did travel in straight lines. Instead, there would just be two bright lines directly opposite the slits in the screen. Diffraction has taken place as the light squeezed its way through the very narrow slits; the light has spread out on either side and the two sets of waves were able to overlap and interfere. This combination of diffraction and interference is an important part of the laser-based technique for reconstructing three-dimensional images, which is described in Chapter 4.

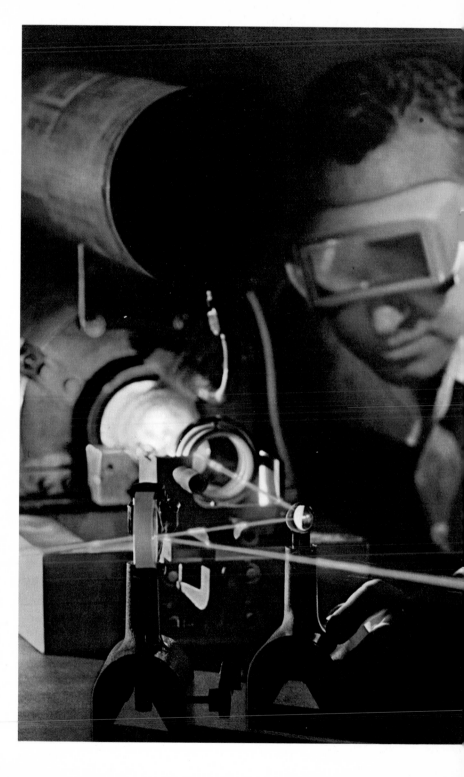

2 Types of Laser

In the paper that Arthur L. Schawlow and Charles H. Townes wrote in 1958 (see page 20), in which they showed on theoretical grounds that laser action should be possible, they described a system in which the active material was potassium vapor enclosed in a tube. It was something of a surprise when the first laser ever made, two years later, turned out to contain a solid active material—ruby—rather than a gaseous one. Schawlow and Townes chose a gas quite deliberately. The molecules in a gas are, for the most part, very well spaced out and far away from each other. Although each one moves about and frequently collides with other molecules, it spends most of its time on its own; or, to put it another way, by far the greatest part of the volume of a gas consists of empty space. This makes it much easier to calculate how the gas will behave when one tries to stimulate the emission of radiation in it, because each molecule can be considered on its own, and there is no need to worry about the influence of other molecules on it. In potassium vapor, each "molecule" is, in fact,

A continuously operating argon laser under test. This type allows the user to choose between six or more different wavelengths in the blue-green region of the visible spectrum.

a single atom, and this makes the calculation of the gas's behavior even simpler, because molecules that are made up of several atoms combined together are more complicated entities than individual atoms.

For these reasons most of the scientists taking part in the race to make the first laser were trying with monatomic gases as the active materials, and Ali Javan of the Bell Telephone Laboratories, together with two of his colleagues, made the first laser of this type toward the end of 1960, only a few months after Maiman's ruby laser appeared. Since 1960, many different kinds of laser have been built, and active materials now include liquids, polyatomic gases, and solids other than ruby. There are now several ways of pumping lasers, and many different wavelengths can be produced. From the user's point of view, each laser has advantages and disadvantages depending on its application. For instance, ruby lasers and glass lasers produce the highest power (when the giant pulse technique described on page 53 is used), but some other kinds are far more efficient converters of pumping energy into laser energy. Some lasers are useful because they produce continuous beams, or beams that are exceptionally narrow in bandwidth, exceptionally directional, or exceptionally coherent. Others may not be outstanding in any of these respects, but be useful because it is easy to impress a signal onto their beams. Different lasers operate in different parts of the electromagnetic spectrum, and some offer a choice of colors. The argon laser in the photograph on page 36, for example, allows the user to choose between several colors in the blue-green region of the spectrum. In this chapter we shall take a look at the various types of laser existing at the present time, and at one or two others that are still only speculative.

The Helium-Neon Gas Laser

Gas lasers are physically rather different from ruby lasers. The gas or mixture of gases forming the active medium is enclosed in a container formed from glass or quartz with polished mirrors at either end. The laser produced at the Bell Laboratories in late 1960 contained a mixture consisting of about 90 per cent helium and 10 per cent neon.

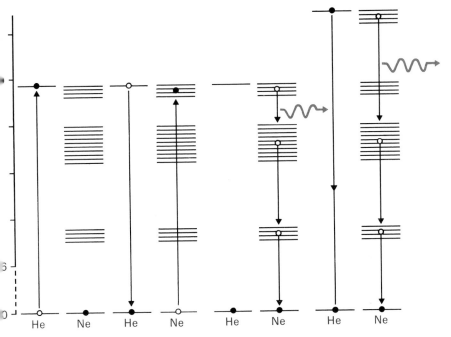

Energy-level diagram for the helium-neon laser. First the helium atom is excited to a level just below 20 ev., then it transfers its energy to a neon atom, exciting it to one of a group of closely spaced levels. The neon atom falls to the ground state in stages, the first stage being the laser transition. The radiation is in the infrared part of the spectrum, but visible radiation can be produced using a higher group of levels in neon, as shown in the right-hand part of the diagram.

The wave packets making up the laser beam come from the neon atoms. The great problem in early attempts to make neon lasers was finding a way of pumping the neon atoms so that they could be raised to an excited state. This was solved by the Bell Telephone Research Group by adding the helium gas and exciting it with a small radio transmitter. The electric and magnetic fields created by the transmitter cause the helium atoms to move about rapidly and acquire enough energy to be raised to an excited state. By a happy coincidence, this excited state coincides exactly with an excited state of neon, so whenever a helium atom in the excited state collides with a neon atom in the ground state it can transfer all its energy to the neon atom, as shown in the diagram on page 39. The collisions occur very frequently in a gas mixture at sufficiently high pressure, so that a population inversion can be produced and maintained. The neon atoms are now capable of amplifying light by stimulated emission, the end mirrors provide reflecting surfaces for bouncing the beam backward and forward through the gas, and so a laser beam builds up just as in the ruby crystal used by Maiman.

Unlike the earlier ruby laser, which produced only pulses of light, the gas laser operates continuously. It has a much lower power output than the ruby laser, but is almost perfectly coherent. It can be controlled more precisely and so is particularly useful for communication purposes.

Visible Light from Gas Lasers

Improvements were made in the helium-neon gas laser during the next two years. Other noble gases were used, and so was atomic oxygen. But all these lasers, including Javan's, produced infrared, and therefore invisible, beams. Real interest in the gas laser was aroused only after the discovery that a helium-neon laser could be made to produce a beam in the red part of the visible spectrum, for with continuous visible laser beams many new and unexpected effects were observed.

In spite of this discovery, it became clear over the next few years that gas lasers of the type produced so far were primarily sources of infrared beams, and there seemed little possibility of obtaining laser beams in the visible and ultraviolet parts of the spectrum. Indeed, there seemed to be theoretical reasons why gas lasers could not produce such beams. Ordinary gas atoms emit wave packets of comparatively low energy, whereas wave packets of large energy are needed to produce the higher frequency, shorter wavelength beams in the visible and ultraviolet parts of the electromagnetic spectrum.

It was, therefore, a very important milestone in the development of the laser when the American scientist W. E. Bell announced that he had produced a visible laser beam using mercury gas as the active material. The gas was made up not of ordinary mercury atoms but of mercury *ions*. An atom consists of a heavy positively charged nucleus around which a number of negatively charged electrons revolve. It looks rather like a miniature solar system, with the sun corresponding to the nucleus and the planets to the electrons. In a normal mercury atom, the positive charge of the nucleus at the center is exactly balanced by the total negative charge of the 80 electrons in orbit around it, so that the whole atom is electrically neutral. However, it is fairly easy to remove one of the outermost electrons and when this is done the atom is left with a small net positive charge. Such an atom is then called an *ion*.

The importance of ions as far as lasers are concerned is that they have energy levels different from their parent neutral atoms, so they are potential sources of new wavelengths. Mercury ion lasers failed to live up to their early promise as high-power sources of red and green laser beams, but other types of ionized gases, argon in particular, have proved very effective. Today, not only do ion lasers cover the whole of the visible spectrum, but continuous and pulse operation on wavelengths in the near ultraviolet have been achieved.

The early ion lasers were pumped not by radio transmitters but by electron beams, which were also used to ionize the gas. An electron beam is formed by heating a metallic cathode up to the point at which electrons are "boiled" off its surface (hence the name "cathode rays," which is sometimes given to such beams). These electrons are then accelerated to high speeds and focused into a dense beam by a system of positively charged plates. When this high-speed beam strikes atoms of argon or some other gas, it knocks electrons out of them and also raises the newly ionized atoms to excited states.

The trouble with this method of ionizing and pumping the laser system was that it also physically pumped gas from one end of the laser tube to the other. This problem was solved by fitting a return pipe to equalize the pressures at the two ends of the laser tube. A further improvement was made by using a longitudinal magnetic field through the tube to concentrate the electrons and so produce a laser beam of greater power.

Unfortunately, ion lasers using this type of system proved to have very short lives. There were two reasons for this. In all lasers, cooling arrangements are necessary to carry away the heat that is a by-product of the lasing process, and in the type of construction used in early ion lasers the area of the laser tube in contact with the cooling medium was very small. The power that could be obtained was restricted and the laser was liable to overheat. The second reason, which was even more important, was the bombardment of the cathode and the walls of the tube by the positively charged ions, which caused these components to fail very quickly.

One promising way around this difficulty that has been applied recently is to use a radio transmitter instead of an electron beam. Radio transmitters are used with helium-neon lasers, as we saw on page 39, but the technique adopted with ion lasers is somewhat different because the gas has to be ionized as well as pumped. The transmitter this time causes an electrical discharge to form right round the tube, through both the laser section and the return pipe. Laser action itself takes place only between the end mirrors. There is now no delicate cathode to be damaged, and bombardment of the walls of the tube is reduced. All this serves to lengthen the life of the laser greatly. It also means that highly reactive gases such as chlorine can be used as the active material. Chlorine is almost as efficient as argon and is an excellent gas for use in lasers, but it cannot be used in systems employing an electron-beam pumping system because it would destroy the cathode.

A Laser Workhorse

In 1965 came the first announcement of the *molecular gas laser*, a new type that seems destined to be the laser workhorse in the industrial, military, and research fields. The molecular laser produces more power and is more efficient than other gas lasers, and one type can, for example, crumble rocks and fracture granite, and set fabrics on fire at a substantial distance.

The earlier types of gas laser are very inefficient converters of pumping energy into laser energy because of the way the atoms return from the excited state to the ground state. In the helium-neon laser, for example, the diagram on page 39 shows that the

Small and large lasers. Right: a miniature gas laser that operates continuously when placed in an appropriate optical cavity. Below: a 33-foot gas laser that, because of its length, produces very great amplification every time the beam travels down the tube. The tube can be emptied and refilled with various gases.

excited neon atoms return to the ground state in a number of steps, giving up energy at each one. Only one of these steps contributes to the laser beam. The energy given up in the other steps is wasted, appearing as nonlaser light, heat, etc.

In 1965 C. K. N. Patel, a scientist at the Bell Telephone Laboratories, found that gas lasers could be made more efficient if the gas consisted of heavy molecules rather than of single atoms. A new type of laser structure was needed because the pumping techniques used in other gas lasers tend to break molecules down into their individual atoms. Patel devised a system, the *flowing-gas structure*, in which the gas flows continuously into the region between the two mirrors and there meets a flow of nitrogen gas that has previously been excited by electrical or

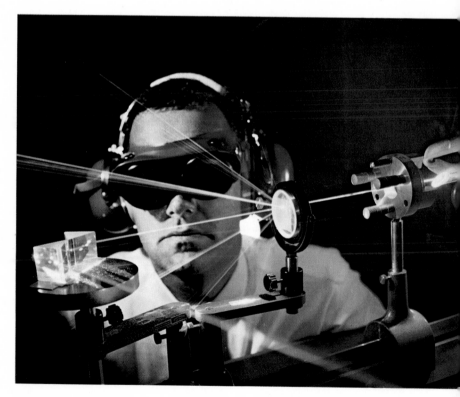

electron-beam discharge. When the two gases meet, energy is transferred from the nitrogen atoms to the heavy molecules of the active gas.

Patel used the flowing-gas structure to demonstrate lasers based on carbon monoxide, carbon dioxide, nitrous oxide, and carbon disulfide. The highest efficiency of all was obtained with carbon dioxide, and later work showed that this gas was unique in being chemically stable enough to function when the pumping source excites it directly. Thus carbon dioxide lasers, which have come to be the accepted type of molecular laser, do not have to have the flowing-gas arrangement; but, as we shall see, it still has some advantages. Patel himself got efficiencies of about 15 per cent, which compares very well with the efficiencies

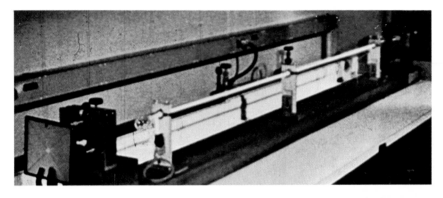

Opposite: a continuous wave gas laser in operation.

Above: a helium-neon gas laser of the type that operates in the visible region of the spectrum.

Right: the beam from a helium-neon gas laser operating in the infrared (invisible) part of the spectrum is displayed as a green spot on an image converter tube.

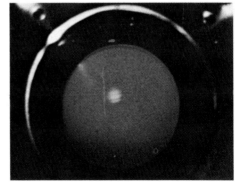

of less than 0.1 per cent achieved with single-atom gas lasers. With carbon dioxide molecules, the energy given up to the laser beam is a significant proportion of the total energy lost as the excited molecule returns to the ground state. Later work by Patel and other people showed that adding traces of different gases such as helium increased the efficiency of the carbon dioxide laser still further.

By early 1967, commercial exploitation of the carbon dioxide laser was well under way. North American Aviation Inc. had demonstrated a carbon dioxide laser with an output of 4000 W. and the Raytheon Company's research division had announced one with an efficiency of 17 per cent capable of producing 1200 W. This laser is formed from two 10-meter-long tubes, which are parallel and optically coupled to give an effective laser length of 20 meters. This laser can fracture granite and burn holes in bones. The radiant energy density of these carbon dioxide lasers, which operate continuously, is much higher than that of the sun.

To get large amounts of power, the path between the end mirrors of a carbon dioxide laser must be as long as possible. If such a long laser is to be practical for mobile uses on land or in the air, the tube must be folded in the way the Raytheon Company's tube was folded. Techniques like this enable the designer to maintain the laser's effective length while containing it in a small package. In the middle of 1967, a Company in Palo Alto, California, had ready for production a 500-W. carbon dioxide laser that could be made up of either three or four tubes placed parallel to each other.

Although a flowing-gas system does not have to be used with carbon dioxide, such a system does have a number of advantages. With a closed, sealed-off system, or with a recirculating system, the gas tends to form undesired compounds after a while. Sealed-off systems are simpler to design than flowing-gas systems but produce only about one third as much power.

A 1200-W. carbon dioxide laser is being used to make rocks and granite crumble in civil engineering experiments at the Massachusetts Institute of Technology. Carbon dioxide lasers may also be used one day to help in drilling underground tunnels, a possibility now being investigated as part of the technical studies on a high-speed underground transportation system between Boston and Washington. But, as we shall see in Chapter 7, this is not the kind of job for which lasers are best suited. They face competition from incoherent sources, such as plasma torches, with greater power and efficiency. It is only when the drilling has to be of a particularly precise and accurate nature that the laser scores over its rivals.

Carbon dioxide lasers produce a beam on a wavelength of 106,000 A., which is well into the infrared part of the spectrum. Although this is not within the visible part of the electromagnetic spectrum, it is a particularly important wavelength for communication applications because, as we shall see in Chapter 3, it penetrates the atmosphere very well.

The high power of the carbon dioxide laser and the fact that it produces a wavelength that penetrates the atmosphere make it particularly suitable for relaying live television pictures from the surface of a planet or from space vehicles passing close to such a planet. The pictures of the surface of the planet Mars taken by the Mariner space craft had to be transmitted point by point over many days because of the extremely low power output of the received radio signal. It seems likely that, if a carbon dioxide laser and its associated power supplies could be built into a space probe, it would be able to transmit televised pictures of the surface of Mars as soon as the camera was switched on. The laser beam would not penetrate cloud in the upper atmosphere of the earth so the signals would probably have to be transmitted to a cloud-free area or reflected by an earth satellite to a receiving station in such an area.

Solid Lasers

As we saw at the beginning of this chapter, it was something of a surprise when the first practical laser turned out to be one that used a solid crystal as the active material, because the way light interacts with the densely packed atoms in a solid was not understood nearly as well as the way it interacts with the relatively isolated atoms found in a gas. This is a very good example of the fact that in science one does not necessarily have to understand processes fully in order to make a practical working device. Although nobody in 1960 understood in every detail the process that goes on in a ruby laser—and perhaps nobody does even now—it had been shown fairly conclusively from experimental observations on ruby that this crystalline substance had the sort of characteristics that would allow laser action to take place inside it.

Ruby consists of aluminum oxide with a small amount of chromium dissolved in it. The chromium is in the form of positively charged ions, written as Cr^{+++} to indicate that the atom has lost three of its outer electrons. The energy-level diagram on page 22 refers specifically to this type of chromium ion. The synthetic rubies used in lasers are formed by melting aluminum oxide and chromium in a crucible and inserting into the melt a tiny crystal of ruby, to act as a seed crystal. A large crystal starts to grow around the seed and this is drawn out slowly with a steady spiral motion from the glowing white-hot melt.

Some months before announcing that he had produced a ruby laser, Maiman published a paper called "Optical and Microwave-Optical Experiments in Ruby," in which he described the properties of ruby that make it suitable for use in a laser. He showed that its characteristic red color is due to the absorption of blue, green, and yellow light, as explained on page 23. Only the red part passes through and is seen, Furthermore, the red color is enhanced to some extent by *fluorescent emission*—the energy absorbed from the yellow, green, and blue light being converted into red light by the chromium ions. It was a close examination of these characteristics that convinced Maiman that it was worth trying to get laser action from ruby.

It is very unusual for a solid at ordinary temperatures to absorb and emit light in this way, but it has been known for centuries that a few special solid substances can do it. We know now that these substances consist of a very small percentage of one type of atom dissolved in a *host crystal* made up of atoms of a quite different type. In the case of ruby, the host crystal is the aluminum oxide, and the amount of chromium dissolved in it is about five hundredths of one per cent. The host crystal serves purely as a medium in which the chromium ions, which are the ones that emit the light, can be suspended. The concentration of

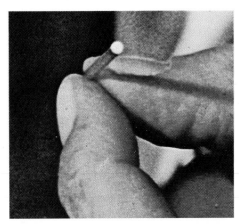

Construction of a solid-state laser. Above: the flashtube. Right: the active material, a crystal of calcium tungstate neodymium with a reflecting coating on its ends. Below: the crystal and flashtube are housed in a container whose internal wall is an elliptical mirror for focusing the pumping energy onto the crystal.

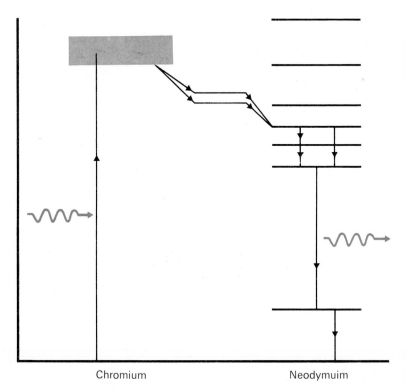

Chromium   Neodymuim

Sensitization is a technique for combining the useful properties of different types of atom. Neodymium has the narrow levels that make for good emission characteristics, but it has no broad absorption bands. Chromium, on the other hand, has a broad pumping band. When the two are used together in a laser, the chromium absorbs energy from the pumping source and the neodymium emits it as a laser light.

chromium must be low to ensure that the distance between individual chromium ions is great, just as is the case with the atoms of a gas. Furthermore, the chromium ions have a rather peculiar atomic structure that serves to screen their vibrations to some extent from the effects of neighboring atoms.

Maiman's demonstration of the effectiveness of ruby as a laser material encouraged scientists to look for other solid materials that could be used. The dissolved atoms—the *activator atoms,* as they are called—would have to have the same kind of atomic structure, with its screening effect, as chromium atoms. There are three groups of elements that immediately appear to be suitable. One is the group known as the *rare earths*. Of these, neodymium (dissolved in yttrium aluminum garnet) is the easiest to operate in a laser, and two others—samarium and europium—also emit laser light in the visible part of the spectrum. Other rare earths have been used in lasers producing infrared radiation.

Chromium itself is one of the *transition metals* and it might seem reasonable to think that some of the other elements in this group would make useful activators. In fact, though, little success has been achieved with them. The third group of elements with the appropriate type of atom structure is the *actinides*. Included in this series are uranium, the heaviest element found in nature, and the various man-made transuranium elements such as plutonium. Some of the actinides—uranium in particular—have been successfully used in lasers. Calcium fluoride, calcium tungstate, and yttrium aluminum garnet are popular host crystals for the rare earths and for the actinide group of elements.

Glass Lasers

Ruby is an outstanding laser material largely because of its mechanical hardness and its high thermal conductivity, the latter allowing the waste heat produced during the laser action to be carried away quickly. Except for very large systems it is still the most important laser material for high-power operation, but it does have a serious competitor in this field in the glass laser. Glass differs from the other solid host materials we have met in being a noncrystalline substance. It is particularly useful as a host material because it is easy and cheap to produce in the sizes and shapes needed for high-power operation. Its optical qualities are excellent, needless to say, and there is a highly developed glass technology already in existence.

Glass does, however, have a rather poor thermal conductivity, and this restricts the maximum output when the laser is operating continuously or at a high pulse repetition rate. The beam from a glass laser has a somewhat greater bandwidth than that from a ruby laser. But the glass laser's efficiency can be somewhat higher than the ruby laser's and in some respects glass is better than

Left: the crystals used in lasers require great skill in manufacture. Here a crystal of the garnet family, intended for use in a laser, is grown from a melt at 1 900°C.

Opposite: glass lasers. The upper photograph shows an opened-up unit, in which the nearer tube is the flash-tube, the farther one the neodymium glass rod surrounded by a water jacket. The lower photograph is of a neodymium glass rod by itself.

ruby in a laser used to produce giant pulses of very short duration. For the most part glass and the crystal hosts complement each other.

The rare earth neodymium is the most important activator atom—or rather, ion, since it is the triply charged Nd^{+++} that is actually employed—used with glass hosts, and the neodymium-in-glass laser is an efficient laser that can operate at room temperature. An interesting technique known as sensitization, illustrated on page 50, has proved particularly effective with glass hosts. The glass contains not just neodymium but also some chromium. The chromium absorbs light and transfers it to the neodymium, and it is only the atoms of the latter element that emit energy into the laser beam. The chief advantage of this process is that chromium absorbs light over a much broader band of wavelengths than neodymium does and so the laser makes better use of the energy available from the pumping source. In another laser using this technique, the glass contains four different types of rare-earth atom dissolved in it—thulium,

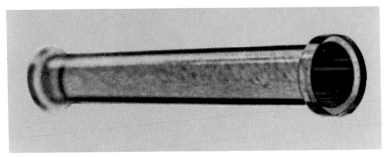

ytterbium, and erbium, which all absorb light energy from the pumping source, and holmium, which takes energy from the other types of atom and emits it into the laser beam.

Giant Pulses

By far the most powerful laser pulses of all are produced by the so-called *giant-pulse technique*, also known as *Q-switching*. This technique depends on the fact that when atoms are raised to an excited state they remain there for perhaps a few thousandths of a second—a relatively long time compared to the times normally involved in laser action.

Initially, the optical path between the laser mirrors is blocked so that lasing cannot occur. The active material is pumped by a powerful light source so that a very high proportion of its atoms are excited. The block in the optical path is then removed: laser action starts, and all the stored energy is emitted in one intense pulse. This pulse can last for anything from one hundred millionth of a second to one ten millionth of a second—far

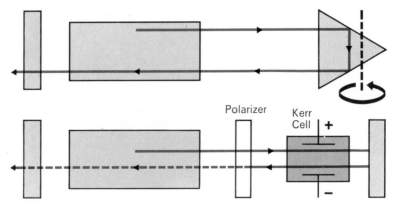

Polarizer   Kerr Cell

Top: Q-switching using a rotating prism. Lasing can occur only when the prism is in the position shown. Bottom: Q-switching using a Kerr cell. When the electric field in the cell is switched on, the light returning from the mirror is blocked by the polarizer, and lasing is prevented.
Opposite page: a laser with a chemical Q-switch, contained in the box on the left of the picture.

shorter than the pulses produced by ordinary techniques.

Most of this giant-pulse work has been done with ruby lasers. The power intensity is so enormous that it has been known to produce irreversible damage in the ruby crystal itself. Commercial units capable of surviving many pulses of somewhat lower power are now available, the most powerful, in early 1968, being a 10-GW laser (1 gigawatt$=10^9$ W.) manufactured by the Compagnie Générale d'Electricité, of Paris.

There are several ways of blocking and unblocking the optical path between the mirrors, two of which are illustrated on this page. The top diagram shows one of the earliest systems used. An end reflector—a prism or a mirror—is mounted on a rotating shaft and laser action can only start when the rotation of the shaft brings the reflector into alignment with the laser material and the second reflector. Other systems have used electro-optic devices that change their optical characteristics under the influence of an applied voltage. The second diagram on page 54 shows one such system employing a *Kerr cell*. This contains a transparent material that, when there is a voltage across it,

changes the state of polarization of light passing through it by an amount determined by the strength of the field. The polarizer blocks all the light except that with one particular plane of polarization, and the system is arranged so that lasing can occur only when the electric field is switched off.

Semiconductor Lasers

All the lasers described so far, including the carbon dioxide laser, are inefficient converters of pumping energy into laser energy. This is not a very serious disadvantage in all applications, but it does restrict the use of these lasers in mobile applications on earth and in space because of the great weight of the power supply needed with them. Fortunately there is another type of laser, the semiconductor laser, which seems likely to be the means of overcoming this problem, because it has already been operated with efficiencies of 30 to 40 per cent—two or three times as great as that of the carbon dioxide laser—and it seems likely that efficiencies approaching 100 per cent will eventually become possible.

Semiconductors are a special class of substance that, as their name implies, have electrical conductivities in between those of the common conductors and the common insulators. One of these semiconductors—gallium phosphide—had interested physicists and engineers for many years before semiconductor lasers were first made, because of the scintillations of bright red light that were observed when a current was passed through it. Other semiconductor materials containing gallium and arsenic compounds were later found to give off infrared rays when a current flowed through them, and a group at MIT's Lincoln Laboratory used these infrared rays to send television pictures over a short distance. Later on they were able to send messages between two Massachusetts hilltops 30 miles apart. The rays used in these experiments were, of course, made up of ordinary incoherent waves, and no laser action was involved.

The scintillations showed that these semiconductors were somehow converting the energy of the current into photons of electromagnetic radiation, and at the beginning of the 1960s it became clear that laser action might be possible if the current was made large enough. This laser action was actually achieved late in 1962 by three independent research teams in the United States: Robert N. Hall, G. E. Fenner, J. D. Kingsley, T. J. Soltys and R. O. Carlson of the General Electric Company, T. M. Quist, R. H. Rediker, Robert J. Keyes, William E. Krag, Benjamin Lax, Alan McWhorter and Herbert J. Zeiger of the Lincoln Laboratory, and M. Nathan, W. P. Dumke, Gerald Burns, F. H. Dill and Gordon Lasher of the International Business Machines Corporation. The current density had to be around 10,000 amperes per square centimeter, and to achieve this the semiconductors were cooled down to the temperature of liquid nitrogen.

The first diagram on page 58 shows the energy levels of a normal semiconductor, or rather, the energy bands, since that is what they are. The lower band, called the *valence band*, is separated from the upper *conduction band* by a gap representing a range of energies forbidden to the electrons in the semiconductor. In the ground state, all the electrons would be in the valence band and none at all in the conduction band. This is the situation shown in the diagram, where gray shading indicates an electron population. In fact this situation would exist only at or very close to the absolute zero of temperature, and at normal temperatures some electrons would have been promoted to the conduction band, leaving behind "holes" in the valence band. The number of these holes is obviously equal to the number of electrons in the conduction band.

By adding a very small percentage of a suitable impurity it is possible to achieve a situation in which there are *more* electrons in the conduction band than there are holes in the valence band. Such a "doped" semiconductor is called N-type. In its ground state all the electrons that can will crowd into the valence band, but there will still be some in the conduction band; this is shown in the second diagram on page 58. If a different type of impurity is used instead, the material may have an excess of holes in the valence band, as shown in the third diagram, which again represents the ground state (zero temperature) situation. This kind of semi-conductor is called P-type.

The situation of interest to us is shown in the fourth, and largest, of the diagrams, which shows the energy bands at the boundary between an N-type region and a P-type region. There is a transition region, perhaps only a few hundred angstroms thick, where a population inversion exists and electrons in the conduction band can fall down and occupy holes in the valence band, emitting photons of electromagnetic radiation.

The material is joined to a power supply acting in a direction to make electrons in the N-type region move toward the junction region. Large numbers of electrons cross the junction when the current is flowing so only a small slice of semiconductor material is needed, perhaps as small as one square millimeter in area. Semiconductor lasers of this type are also known as *junction lasers*, *junction diode lasers*, and *injection lasers* (because electrons are injected into the junction region).

The construction of a semiconductor laser is shown on page 60. Laser action takes place in the thin junction region and the beam is made directional by the highly polished end faces, which act as mirrors. The reason these lasers are so efficient is that nearly every electron injected contributes a useful photon. They have other advantages too. Because their output power is controlled by the supply voltage, the beam can easily be made to carry sounds or pictures. A little while after the first discovery of these lasers, one was made that operated at room temperature— instead of the temperature of liquid nitrogen—on a wavelength of 9000 A., which is in the near infrared. As the temperature is decreased the wavelength drops to about 8400 A., so these

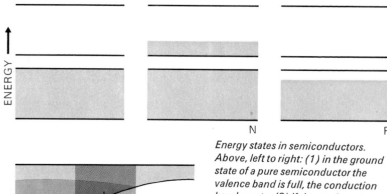

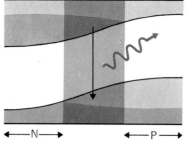

Energy states in semiconductors. Above, left to right: (1) in the ground state of a pure semiconductor the valence band is full, the conduction band empty; (2) if the semiconductor is doped with N-type impurities the excess electrons occupy the lowest states of the conduction band; (3) if doped with P-type impurities, there are "holes" in the top of the valence band. Left: if an N-type and a P-type region meet, there is a population inversion in the junction region.

lasers can be tuned by varying the temperature.

This tunability is not wholly advantageous because it means that the laser cannot give an accurately reproducible wavelength. Semiconductor lasers have a lower power output than solid lasers, and their beams spread over a greater range of wavelengths than the beams from gas lasers, but their advantages are enough to ensure an important place for them in spite of these snags.

Nick Holonyak Jr. and S. F. Bevacqua of the General Electric Company obtained other wavelengths by using as their semiconductor not just gallium arsenide—as in the early versions—but a three-element alloy mixture of gallium, arsenic, and phosphorus. By varying the ratio of arsenic to phosphorus, the wavelength could be varied between about 6100 and 8400 A. Schawlow has suggested that a mixture of gallium, indium, and arsenic could produce wavelengths between 8400 and 31,000 A., thus extending laser operation well into the far infrared.

The great difficulty with junction lasers is to make them. Laser action takes place along the line of the junction, which is extremely narrow—perhaps only a few hundred angstroms thick, as we have said. It must be exceptionally straight for to-and-fro reflections to occur. Such a perfectly straight junction is very difficult to achieve, and this difficulty has led to the development of three other pumping methods that do not need a junction. The first uses a high-energy electron beam. If a beam of electrons is accelerated by a potential difference of 20,000 V. or more and directed at the flat face of a semiconductor, the electrons will penetrate the material for a distance of several thousand angstroms, strike groups of atoms in the semiconductor, and cause electrons in the outermost atomic shells to break free. So great is the energy of the beam that about 10,000 such electrons are freed by every beam electron. Each free electron then wanders through the semiconductor material until it meets a group of atoms that has earlier had an electron knocked out by the beam. The free electron is captured by this group of atoms, and a wave packet is emitted in the process.

An alternative to electron-beam pumping is optical pumping. The semiconductor is illuminated by a high-energy light source that frees electrons from groups of atoms. One difficulty with this method is that the light may not penetrate very far into the semiconductor materials, and three Russian scientists, N. G. Basov, A. Z. Grasyuk, and V. A. Katulin, overcame this by actually using a laser as the pumping source. They used a special ruby laser to pump a gallium arsenide semiconductor laser in this way, and devised a technique for shifting the wavelength of the ruby laser beam so that its energy was close to a value that could be absorbed by the atoms in the semiconductor. By this method they obtained a laser beam with a power of 30,000 W. from the gallium arsenide.

One of these Russian scientists, Basov (who, incidentally, published one of the earliest papers describing experiments on stimulated emission, in the early 1950s), proposed the third of the pumping techniques that avoid the use of a P–N junction and its attendant problems. In this technique, an electric field of great strength is used to accelerate any free electrons that may already be in the material. These electrons reach tremendous velocities and give up enough energy in collisions with groups of atoms to cause bound electrons to break free. As with electron-beam pumping, many bound electrons are freed by each accelerated electron, and when they are recaptured they give up wave packets to the laser beam. This process is called *avalanche breakdown*.

From Flames to X rays

The three types of laser discussed in this chapter so far—the gas laser, the solid laser, and the semiconductor laser—are by far the most important; but several others are possible and some of them have already been demonstrated in the laboratory.

Some organic liquids can be used as the active material. The great advantage of using a liquid is that it is very easy to cool, by circulating it so as to bring overheated areas regularly into contact with the cooling surface. It is also easy to make rapid wavelength changes by simply changing the liquid in the container. Benzene, nitrobenzene, and pyridine are liquids that have been used, and so have organic chelates incorporating rare-earth elements such as europium as activators.

Construction of a junction diode laser. The active material is gallium arsenide phosphide, doped to make it P-type in one part, N-type in the rest. The end faces of the diode are polished to make them act as mirrors.

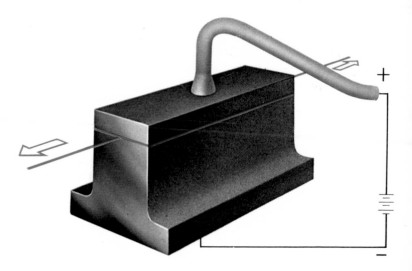

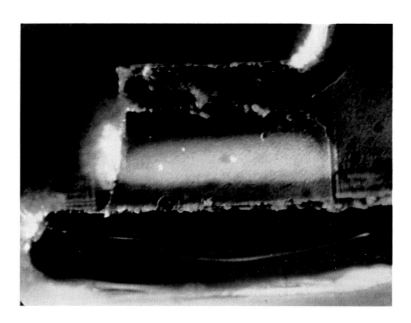

The glowing junction strip of a gallium arsenide laser in action.

Chemical reactions have long served to illuminate the dwellings of man, and it seems reasonable to expect that this method of producing photons will be used in lasers. Many different kinds of chemical reaction are being investigated with this in mind, but there are still serious problems to be solved before a useful flame laser can be made.

One of the most fascinating possibilities is the development of lasers working in the very short wavelength parts of the electromagnetic spectrum, such as the X-ray and gamma-ray bands. It seems likely that if such lasers could be produced their effect would be every bit as great as that of the earlier lasers, perhaps even greater. The enormously intense narrow beam of X rays from an X-ray laser would be of immense value to the surgeon; and would also probably at last produce that long-sought-after weapon, the deathray. An X-ray laser would probably also be able to destroy an incoming ballistic missile, and the availability of relatively cheap X-ray lasers might thus provide even small nations with a foolproof ballistic missile defense system, with profound effects on the political and military balance in the world.

All this is still very speculative, however, and indeed it seemed for a while as though there were theoretical barriers to the production of an X-ray laser. The difficulty was to visualize how mirrors could be constructed for a laser working at such short wavelengths. Conventional mirror structures of the kind used with visible light are quite out of the question, and this led many physicists to believe that an X-ray laser could never be produced. Then, in the middle of 1967, experiments carried out at the Bell Telephone Laboratories by W. L. Bond, M. A. Dugnay, and P. M. Betzepis showed that it might be possible to construct an X-ray laser using the actual molecular structure of a crystal as the mirrors of the system.

These scientists pointed out that for one particular direction the molecular planes of perfect, or very nearly perfect, germanium crystals reflect X rays very efficiently. This led them to propose a ring-like mirror system of a type similar to that used in optical interferometers, but of course much smaller. The system would be in the form of a flat ring and the X-ray beam would travel round and round the ring instead of backward and forward as in the laser systems we have discussed so far. Unfortunately, the nature of the molecular reflection process is such that a simple flat ring would probably be too difficult to make. But the crystal could be deformed to the shape of a 3-dimensional polygon so that it would be, in effect, a puckered ring, and such a ring could, at least in theory, be "tuned" until the X rays were reflected in the desired manner and with the minimum loss at each reflection.

The adjustment, even of the puckered ring, would still be extremely difficult, and a more practicable—though less efficient—mirror structure could be produced from a cubic crystal such as a block of perfect germanium or, possibly, silicon. The mirror system would be produced by making a square hole along the axis of a single block of germanium, and the X-ray laser beam could be extracted in one of several ways. For instance, one side could be made thin enough to be partially transparent to X rays in much the same sort of way as one of the mirrors in conventional lasers is made semitransparent.

This announcement of a possible X-ray laser structure, which came at a time when many experts thought that such lasers were impossible, is a good example of the tremendous swings that have occurred in scientists' ideas of what future laser development might bring.

The laser deathray and the laser anti-ballistic-missile system are two applications that have seemed fairly close at times and have then been shown to be theoretically so unlikely as not to be worth considering. Developments a few years later have then removed the difficulties previously thought to be inherent, and so the processes have gone on.

Despite these uncertainties, the laser has now established itself as a practical tool in many fields and is, as we shall see, already bringing great benefits to surgeons, military planners, photographers, entertainers, engineers, and research scientists exploring still further the complexities of atomic and molecular structures.

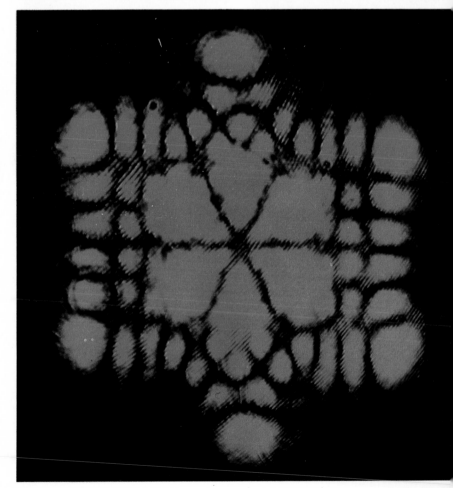

3 Communicating by Light Beam

When the first laser was demonstrated, few people were more excited by it than the scientists and engineers working in the field of communications. The tremendous expansion of the telephone system and television networks that took place during the 1950s, and the prospect of vast numbers of computers talking to each other over telephone wires in the near future, made them fear that there would soon be more television channels, more telephone conversations, and more data links than could be carried by even the most complex conventional system currently at their disposal. The laser now looks as though it may have removed this danger for ever.

The simplest way to send information from one place to another is to talk or shout. The larynx vibrates, makes neighboring air molecules vibrate as well, and starts a sound wave that travels through the air until it strikes the eardrum of someone listening. The resulting vibrations of the eardrum are a close copy of the air vibrations leaving the speaker's mouth. Obviously we cannot

Mode patterns produced on a photographic plate in front of a helium-neon gas laser when a pair of wire cross hairs was placed in the optical cavity. The different patterns correspond to different angles between the wires, so this could be the basis of a future method of modulating a laser beam. The laser used in making these patterns was the one illustrated on page 45.

send messages very far like this, and it is better to convert the sound waves into some other form of energy that travels farther. One way, used in telephone systems, is to employ electrical signals. The basis of this method is that it is possible to produce an electrical analogue of speech. Just as vibrations of the larynx are turned into sound waves that are an analogue of the vibrations, so the sound waves themselves can be turned into electrical waves. In one case the fluctuating quantity is air pressure, in the other it is the current in a wire. The instrument that turns a fluctuating air pressure into a fluctuating electric current is the microphone, and at the receiving end the electrical signals are turned back into sound waves by another instrument, the loudspeaker. In this way speech can be sent along wires.

In a telephone system within a city, it is usual for a single pair of wires to carry the electrical analogue of the speech from a telephone to the local exchange, and for another pair to carry the speech from the receiving exchange to the second telephone. Pairs of wires could be used to carry conversations between exchanges or between cities, but quite exorbitant amounts of wire would be needed.

Fortunately a way around this difficulty exists. Human speech contains vibrations ranging in frequency from 10 or 20 cps to many thousands of cps. Communications engineers have found, however, that speech can be understood if only those frequencies between 200 and 4000 cps are transmitted. Furthermore, it is possible, for purposes of transmission, to change the frequency of speech. It is only necessary for the *range* of frequencies to stay the same. Instead of the range from 200 to 4000 cps, a conversation can be carried on a range of (say) 4200 to 8000 cps, although of course it must be changed back to the original frequencies at the hearing end. Highly sophisticated equipment has been developed for changing the frequency of the voice in this way.

The problem of too many wires is solved by using a special pair of wires, called a *coaxial cable*, and transmitting several conversations simultaneously over one such cable. The first speaker is allocated a range of 200 to 4000 cps; the second, 4200 to 8000 cps; the third, 8200 to 12,000 cps; and so on. The highest frequency that a coaxial cable can carry is about 12,000,000 cps, so about 1500 two-way conversations can be transmitted on one cable. Electrical filters at the far end of the link separate the different conversations and change their frequencies back down again.

It may be surprising that several conversations can be transmitted on one cable and then separated, but the following analogy should help to make it plausible. A fairly primitive method of communicating by light beams is to flash signals in Morse code. If two people wanted to send messages simultaneously in the same direction, one of them could use green light, and the other red light. Both messages could be sent along the same path (a hollow tube with reflecting sides, for instance). At the other end, the two messages could be separated simply by using a glass prism, which would refract the green and red light by different amounts and send each along its own path. Green and red light have different frequencies, just like the various speech-signals in a coaxial cable.

Energy can also be sent through great distances in the form of electromagnetic waves. The first to be used were the radio waves (as they came to be called), which are not absorbed by the atmosphere and do not need wires or pipes to guide them. To send a message we must be able to impress an analogue of speech onto the radio waves. This process is called *modulation*, and the diagram below shows an unmodulated electromagnetic wave

An electromagnetic wave (left) and the same wave when it has been modulated with speech (right).

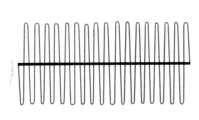
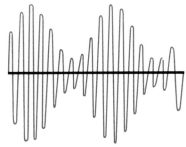

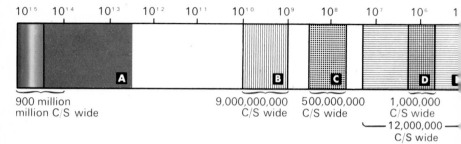

10^{15} 10^{14} 10^{13} 10^{12} 10^{11} 10^{10} 10^{9} 10^{8} 10^{7} 10^{6} 1

A   B   C   D   E

900 million
million C/S wide

9,000,000,000
C/S wide

500,000,000
C/S wide

1,000,000
C/S wide

12,000,000
C/S wide

*Part of the electromagnetic spectrum, showing how the communications space
available in different parts of the spectrum increases enormously with increasing
frequency. The shaded areas represent the visible and infrared regions (A), the
microwave band (B), VHF and UHF television bands (C), medium wave radio
band (D), and coaxial cable band (E). The scale at the top is frequency in cps.*

and the same wave as modulated by a speech waveform. The
modulation process ensures that the radio wave carries the
"information" present in the original speech. As with coaxial
cables, a radio wave can be modulated with several messages, all
of different frequencies, superimposed on each other. They are
eventually separated in the receiver by a filter device, operated
by the tuning knob, which selects a particular band of frequencies.

Radio waves were used before any other electromagnetic waves
because they have low frequencies, and there are technical
reasons for preferring low frequencies to high ones. In the early
days of sound radio, each station was allocated a channel 9000 cps
wide, and many such stations could be occupied on the medium
frequency radio band (also called the medium wave band),
which extends from 550,000 to 1.5 million cps. More "space"—in
terms of information—is available on higher frequencies, and
throughout the history of telecommunications there has been an
upward movement in frequency as new facilities and devices have
been developed. The demand increased enormously with the
advent of television. Just as an analogue of speech can be transmitted in the form of electromagnetic waves, so can an analogue
of a picture, but a much larger band of frequencies is needed.
Bandwidths of 4, 5, and 6 million cps are commonly used for television stations. There is clearly no room for such wide-band
systems in either the medium or the short wave band, and this

forced engineers to use the VHF (Very High Frequency) bands, centered on frequencies of 50 million cps or more. The newest, and highest capacity, communications system so far is the *microwave link*. Microwaves come even farther up the scale than the VHF band, and range from 1000 million to 10,000 million cps. Remembering that a coaxial cable has a bandwidth of 12 million cps, it is clear that a single microwave link can replace several hundred such cables in a telephone system, or, alternatively, carry several television channels in addition to many thousands of telephone conversations. Where can we go after the microwave band has been filled? The region immediately above it in frequency is beyond our present-day technology, but farther up still are the infrared and visible parts of the spectrum. The electromagnetic spectrum on page 13 does not show clearly just how much space is available in these regions. This is because the frequency scale used there is a logarithmic one. The relevant parts are shown on a larger scale opposite. Here too the frequency scale is logarithmic, but the actual widths of different parts of the spectrum are shown alongside the logarithmic scale. The coaxial cable band is 12 million cps wide; the VHF and UHF television bands are some 500 million cps wide; and the microwave part of the spectrum is 9000 million cps wide. The part filled by the visible and near-infrared waves is no less than 900 million million cps wide! Access to this vast unused space is the prospect offered by the laser.

Why Lasers?

Light waves and infrared waves from ordinary sources are practically useless for communications systems because they cannot be modulated by any but the simplest of messages. There is, of course, one well-known way of modulating light beams—Morse code—but it is a very primitive method and, except in special circumstances, not a very useful one.

Conventional light waves are hard to modulate in the same way as radio waves because, as we saw in Chapter 1, ordinary sources do not produce light of a single frequency. We should, in effect, be modulating several transmitters at once and, on being demodulated, the different waves would interfere with each other and produce an intolerable amount of what electronics engineers call "noise." Of course, we could try to isolate a very narrow band of wavelengths by passing light through a prism and then blocking all the wavelengths except for one small range, but the remaining intensity would be far too small to be of use. The only really powerful source of light with a narrow bandwidth is the laser.

This is the main reason for using lasers, but a laser beam has another useful feature—its high directionality. The energy of the beam remains concentrated in a small area for much greater distances than is the case with even the most highly directional radio or microwave beam. Links between planets would be much more reliable and sensitive with lasers than with microwaves. The type of receiver used with lasers would be an *optical antenna*, consisting of a concave mirror focusing the light onto a photo-detector, rather like a car headlight working in reverse. Quite a small antenna of this type would collect a far higher proportion of the energy in a laser beam than would be collected by a much larger radio aerial from a radio beam.

Laser beams are much narrower than radio waves when they leave the source, simply because the laser output aperture is so much smaller than that of a radio transmitter. But they also spread out less. The angle of spread, for any electromagnetic beam, is proportional to the wavelength of the radiation divided by the diameter of the source. A microwave transmitter might radiate on a wavelength of 5 cm. from a 250-cm-diameter horn, whereas a laser beam with a wavelength of 10,000 A. could come from a source of diameter 3 or 4 cm. In the first case the ratio of wavelength to diameter is 1:50, in the second it is 1:30,000!

Neither radio beams nor laser beams begin to spread out as soon as they leave the source. For some distance they travel without any outward spread at all, as shown in the diagram opposite. Once again, it is the diameter of the source and the wavelength of the radiation that determine this distance. For a microwave radio beam it is very short, but for a laser beam it can be as much as a kilometer. Transmitters and receivers in a microwave relay link are usually placed about 100 km. apart. At such distances the receiver picks up only one hundred thousandth of the transmitted power. A laser beam could operate directly over a much longer line-of-sight distance. Alternatively, small lenses placed at intervals of about 1 km. would make it possible to transmit a laser beam with almost no loss over distances as great as those used in microwave relay links.

Communications engineers face two basic problems when they use any kind of electromagnetic wave for sending messages. The first is how to modulate the wave with the message, and demodulate it again later; the second, how to make sure that the wave actually gets from its source to its destination—around corners, if necessary, and without being stopped by anything on the way. In the rest of this chapter, we shall discuss these problems as they apply to laser beams.

Putting Information into a Laser Beam

One of the most promising devices for modulating a laser beam is based on the *electrooptical effect*, discovered by the Scottish physicist John Kerr in 1875. Kerr found that light passing through glass is affected by an electric field. If the glass is placed in such a field, the properties of the light change as it passes through, the extent to which they change depending upon the strength of the field. Thus if the electric field is being produced by a voltage that varies in step with someone's speech rhythm, the outgoing light beam will have this variation imposed upon it, and any modulation in the voltage will be transferred to the light.

Glass is not the only material affected in this way, and it is

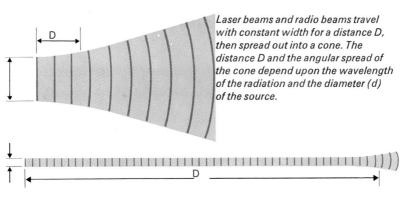

Laser beams and radio beams travel with constant width for a distance D, then spread out into a cone. The distance D and the angular spread of the cone depend upon the wavelength of the radiation and the diameter (d) of the source.

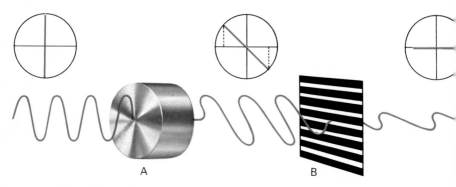

The principle of electrooptical modulation. A wave polarized in the vertical plane passes through a KDP crystal (A) in an electric field. The emerging wave is in a different state of polarization. An analyzer (B) selects a component of this wave whose amplitude is proportional to the strength of the field.

much more convenient, with lasers, to use the solid material potassium dihydrogen phosphate (KDP for short) instead of glass. The property of light affected by the electric field in KDP is its *polarization*. We referred on page 11 to the waves produced in a heavy rope lying on a smooth table when a man holds one end of the rope and shakes his hand from side to side. The vibrations in the rope are all taking place in one plane, and the resulting waves are called *plane-polarized* waves. To be more precise, they are polarized in the horizontal plane. If there were no table, the other end of the rope were tied to a distant tree, and the man shook his hand up and down instead of sideways, the waves would be polarized in the vertical plane. If he moved his hand round and round in a perfect circle the rope would take up a corkscrew appearance; in this case the vibrations are not plane-polarized at all, but *circularly polarized*. If the circle were not perfect, *elliptically polarized* waves, or some even more complicated kind, might result.

All these kinds of polarization can exist in light waves too, and the effect of passing light through KDP when an electric field is switched on is to change its state of polarization. The diagram above shows in a simplified way how a laser beam is modulated. The beam, polarized in the vertical plane, passes through a solid cylinder of KDP and comes out polarized in a different plane. It then meets a *polarizer*, a sheet of material that transmits only light polarized in a particular plane—say, the horizontal plane—and blocks the rest. To go back to the example of the rope, it is as though the rope passed between two horizontal bars very close together, leaving no room for any vertical movement. Whatever the wave traveling along the rope is like to start with, nothing but the horizontally plane-polarized component can get past the bars. The optical polarizer is made of some special material, such as Polaroid, that does just the same thing to light. It behaves like a grating made up of horizontal bars.

When there is no modulating voltage acting on the KDP, no light succeeds in getting through the polarizer, because vertical vibrations have no horizontal component at all. But if there is a voltage, the light emerges from the KDP vibrating in a plane that does have some horizontal component—the amount depending on how strong the field is—and so a modulated laser beam emerges from the system.

The amplitude of the light emerging from the polarizer is directly proportional to the modulating voltage, and changes as

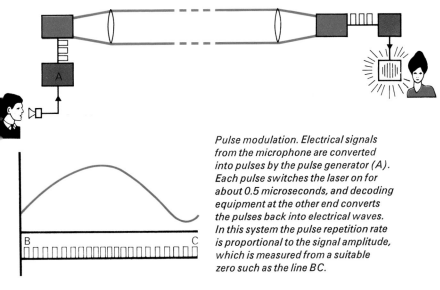

Pulse modulation. Electrical signals from the microphone are converted into pulses by the pulse generator (A). Each pulse switches the laser on for about 0.5 microseconds, and decoding equipment at the other end converts the pulses back into electrical waves. In this system the pulse repetition rate is proportional to the signal amplitude, which is measured from a suitable zero such as the line BC.

74

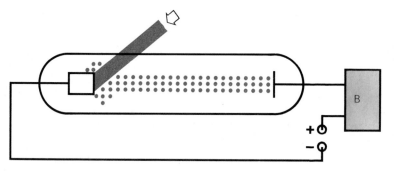

A simple laser-beam demodulator. The laser beam, indicated by the arrow, drives electrons out of the cathode. These electrons are attracted by the positive voltage on the anode and travel through the vacuum, causing a current to flow through the amplifying and reproducing circuits (B).

the amplitude of the speech changes. When information is carried in the form of an amplitude variation like this the wave is said to be *amplitude-modulated*. This is the type of modulation shown on page 67. Anyone familiar with the principles of radio transmission knows that amplitude modulation was the earliest system used, and that there are alternative systems: *frequency modulation*, which is now also used in sound broadcasting, and may also be used in a laser system; and *phase modulation* and *pulse modulation*, both of which are likely to be important in laser communications.

Pulse modulation is illustrated on page 73. The laser is pulsed on and off to generate light pulses with a duration of about half a microsecond each, at a rate of perhaps 2000 per second. The amplitude of the pulses is constant, but their repetition rate varies in step with the variation in the amplitude of the speech. When the amplitude of the sound wave is small, the pulse repetition rate is low. As the amplitude increases, the pulse rate increases, and reaches a maximum when the sound wave amplitude is a maximum.

Pulse modulation will probably be used with lasers that send their signals directly through the atmosphere. As we shall see later (page 81), the atmosphere affects laser beams more than it affects radio waves. Atmospheric turbulence, in particular, would be a serious problem if the laser beam were amplitude-modulated. With pulse modulation, on the other hand, the detector does not have to be continually measuring an amplitude, but only performing the much easier job of deciding whether or not a pulse has arrived.

The laser is a gallium arsenide semiconductor laser set at the focus of a lens aimed at the receiver, as shown on page 73. A second lens at the receiver focuses the light onto a semiconductor. Each time a light pulse impinges on the semiconductor it is absorbed and converted into an electric pulse (the way in which a semiconductor demodulates laser beams is explained on page 77). Electronic circuits then convert the variation in the repetition rate of the pulses into variable-amplitude electrical signals, and these are converted into a replica of the original speech wave by a loudspeaker.

Extracting the Information

One way of extracting the information on an amplitude-modulated laser beam at the receiving site is to direct the beam onto a metal cathode enclosed in a vacuum envelope, as in the diagram

The traveling-wave tube laser demodulator. Electrons driven out of the cathode are accelerated and formed into a beam by the electrodes (A). A current is induced in the coiled wire and flows through the amplifying and reproducing circuits (B).

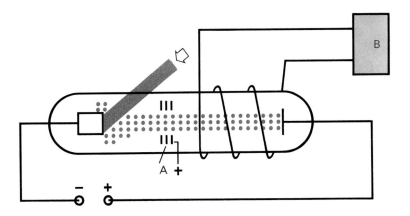

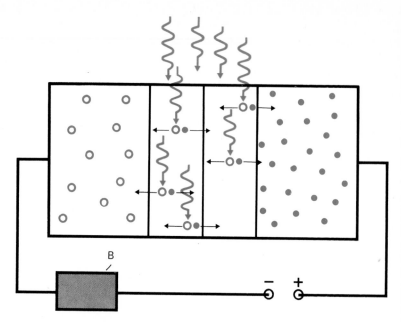

A PN junction demodulator. Wave packets striking the junction release electrons and holes, and cause a current to flow through the amplifying and reproducing circuits (B).

on page 74. As the wave packets in the beam strike the cathode, they knock electrons out of the metal into the surrounding space. If a second electrode, an anode, is placed at the far end of the vacuum envelope and given a very high positive charge it will attract all these electrons. A current will flow in a circuit connected to the anode, and the strength of this current will depend upon the strength of the laser beam. If, for example, the laser beam is modulated with speech, the speech can be reproduced by amplifying the current and using it to control a loudspeaker or the earpiece of a telephone.

A device of this sort is not very sensitive. Links between cities, which carry a lot of messages simultaneously and therefore have large bandwidths, require much more sophisticated demodulating devices. One such device is the *traveling-wave tube cathode detector*, illustrated on page 75. Here, electrons are given off by the cathode as before, and are then accelerated by a series of electrodes into a beam. The intensity of the beam varies in accordance with the modulation. The beam travels down the vacuum tube and passes through a coil of wire around the outside of the tube. The moving electrons induce an electric current in the coil, and almost all the modulation on the beam is transferred to it. This current is then amplified, and the information extracted from it. Another type of demodulator, shown opposite, makes use of the P-N junction between two semiconductors. The semiconductors are connected to a direct-voltage electric supply with the positive side connected to the N-type material and the negative side connected to the P-type material—the opposite of the connection used in the semiconductor laser described in Chapter 2. The excess holes in the P-type material are attracted away from the junction by the negative side of the supply, and the excess electrons in the N-type material are attracted away by the positive side of the supply. In this way, a depletion layer, in which there are no free electrons and no holes, is set up around the junction. The material in this region is therefore a very good insulator, and will not pass electric current. Each time a wave packet of the laser beam strikes it, however, a number of the electrons in the valence band receive enough energy to jump the energy gap. Pairs of holes and conduction electrons are created and immediately swept away in opposite directions by the electric potential, which is very strong in the depletion layer. The arrival of each wave packet causes an electric current to flow in the external circuit, so the strength of the current in this circuit will vary in step with the modulation of the laser beam if it is amplitude-modulated. Alternatively, the P-N junction can be used as a pulse detector if the laser beam is pulse-modulated (as described on page 75).

Both these demodulators are *wide-band devices*: they respond to laser beams on a wide band of wavelengths, and are not wavelength-selective in the way that radio or television sets, or microwave relay receivers, are selective. This has two disadvantages. In an inter-city link it would probably be useful to have several laser beams in one guide, different beams carrying different telephone and television channels. Using two beams, for example, would double the number of channels carried by a single guide. The receivers at the ends of the link would have to be capable of separating the beams by determining their wavelengths, rather like the electrical filters used with coaxial cables (page 67). Wide-band demodulators cannot do this. Furthermore, they pick up any stray visible and infrared radiation ("noise") as well as the laser beam itself, and this reduces the sensitivity of the link. A wavelength-selective receiver would solve both these problems because it would respond only to a very narrow band of wavelengths centered on the wavelength of the wanted laser beam.

Wavelength-selective demodulators operating directly at the wavelength of light would be very difficult to build. Indeed, it is very difficult to build devices of this sort that are capable of working on the shorter of the radio wavelengths. The standard technique used at such wavelengths is the *superheterodyne technique*. The wavelength of the signal is changed, at the receiver input, to a much longer one, and the wavelength-selective circuit needs to operate only at the new wavelength. A similar technique could be used in a laser communications system. The incoming laser beam would be directed onto a wide-band demodulator, and so would a locally produced laser beam of slightly different wavelength. If the demodulator were suitably designed, the output would contain, among other things, a signal whose frequency was equal to the difference between the two laser-beam frequencies. Such a frequency corresponds to a much longer wavelength than the original wavelengths (because low frequency corresponds to large wavelength, as explained on page 14). Selective circuits can be designed to operate at these long wavelengths and so the different messages could be separated.

Laser Beams through the Atmosphere

Having designed systems to modulate and demodulate laser beams, the engineer must consider how the beam is actually to travel from one place on the earth's surface to another. Basically, there are two ways: either in the open, through the atmosphere, or through pipes or tubes. The first method presents far fewer technical problems, but suffers from the fact that light rays and infrared rays can be heavily attenuated as they travel through the air. If laser systems are to be used in. the atmosphere, the wavelengths at which they operate must be chosen very carefully to keep this attenuation to a minimum. The constituents of the atmosphere are oxygen, nitrogen, water vapor, carbon dioxide, ozone, methane, carbon monoxide, and nitrous oxide. Each of them absorbs electromagnetic waves of particular wavelengths, water vapor being the consituent that causes the worst problems with laser beams. The graphs at the top of page 80 show the atmospheric transmission over a 6.5-km. path at sea level on a reasonably clear day. They reveal whole bands of wavelengths that completely fail to penetrate the atmosphere, even over this short distance. However, these graphs are based on measurements made with instruments of fairly low resolving power. This means that a reading does not represent the transmission for a particular wavelength, as it ideally should, but only the average transmission for a relatively wide band of wavelengths. A laser beam, however, spreads over only a very narrow band of wavelengths, and it is possible that there are narrow bands in which the atmospheric absorption is very low and in which a laser beam could be transmitted, that are not revealed by these graphs.

The search for such bands, using instruments of high resolving power, has become an important occupation since the discovery of the laser. Some of the results are shown in the lower graph on page 80. They refer to the region of the spectrum where the ruby laser operates, and do indeed show details not present in the earlier graphs. In particular, there are very narrow bands, some less than one angstrom wide, that are transmitted reasonably well. The peaks and troughs in this graph differ in height by as much as 20 to 1, so the laser wavelength must be chosen very carefully. Fortunately the ruby laser can be tuned over this narrow region in the spectrum by varying the temperature at which it operates.

In addition to the normal constituents of the atmosphere that we have mentioned there are always particles of various sorts suspended in the air, and they will affect a laser link by scattering light out of the beam. The attenuation is worst for big particles and small wavelengths. In hazy conditions, the attenuation is caused mainly by dry particles, which are small compared to the wavelength of light. Much more severe attenuation is caused

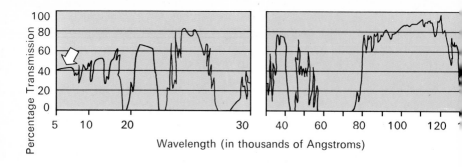

Wavelength (in thousands of Angstroms)

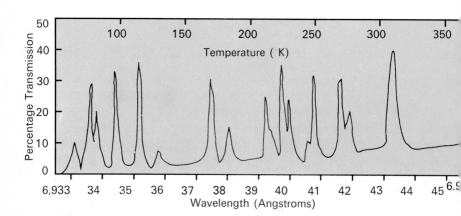

Wavelength (Angstroms)

by stable fogs, which are found near the coast and over the sea. They consist of water that has condensed onto salt nuclei, and their particles are larger than those found in hazes, so that only the longest-wavelength laser beams will penetrate them. In industrial areas the so-called selective fogs occur, whose nuclei are the products of combustion. Selective-fog particles are significantly smaller than those found in stable fogs.

The attenuation due to the various types of particle is shown on the opposite page. But this diagram does not show all the relevant factors. It shows, for instance, that selective fogs cause less attenuation than stable fogs, but the engineer must also take into account the fact that selective fogs occur rather more frequently. In England—an industrial country with a long coastline—one can expect, for about half the time, a visible range as high as 6 km. in the neighborhood of a large town and 19 km. in a good position on the coast.

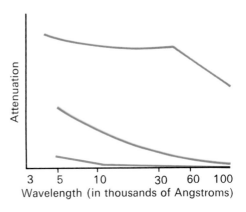

There seems little doubt that, whether the conditions are clear or foggy, there is a good case to be made for using long wavelengths. In conditions of good visibility the signal is attenuated four times as fast on a wavelength of 7000 A. as on a wavelength of 23,600 A. This difference in attenuation rates is even more pronounced in foggy conditions.

Even in good visibility the laser beam can be seriously attenuated by atmospheric turbulence: the splitting-up of large-scale unstable vertical movements of the air causes rapid changes of refractive index and hence random fluctuations in the strength and phase of a laser beam. It is this effect that makes the stars twinkle, and it occurs frequently—though not only—in hot weather. It is the chief reason for using pulse modulation, instead of amplitude or phase modulation, with laser beams that have to travel through the air (see pages 74-5).

For distances less than 6-19 km., depending upon the location (see page 80), the atmospheric laser link promises an attractive new means of communication with advantages where secrecy and light weight are needed. It is very much harder to intercept the highly directional laser beam than to intercept a radio beam; and this has obvious military, and perhaps also commercial, advantages. Laser equipment, because of its low weight, would be easily portable. Even at distances greater than 6-19 km. laser systems might be used if secrecy and light weight were important enough to offset the disadvantage of having the link put out of action by occasional heavy fogs.

For distances greater than those quoted above, a laser beam could travel through the atmosphere only at a height well above that at which fogs, hazes, and turbulence occur. Two methods for achieving this have been suggested. In the first, a laser, a series of lenses, and a receiver would be mounted in balloons anchored high up, and messages would travel from one such balloon to another. In the second, the beam from a ground-based laser would be reflected over the horizon by an object in the sky. Both laser and receiver would be within the layer of the atmosphere in which attenuation can occur; but most of the path would be above this layer. Scientists at the International Telephone and Telegraph Federation laboratories in New Jersey have tried using clouds as the reflecting medium. They found that typical cumulus clouds can scatter the beam to a receiver more than 150 km. from the transmitter. A one-watt laser operating on a wavelength of 7000 A. could carry a considerable amount of information in fair weather conditions. Dense surface fogs would put the link out of action for a very small fraction of the total time, but this would not necessarily have an important effect on the economics of the link. Some clouds or high-level haze (which could also be used to reflect the beam) seem to be present on even the finest days.

This system is rather similar to the tropospheric scatter propagation technique used in beyond-the-horizon microwave radio links. These use the sharp changes in refractive index in the troposphere to scatter the beams. Computer calculations show that the fraction of the power received from a laser beam scattered by a cumulus cloud, although extremely small, would be almost exactly the same as the fraction of the microwave power received in existing tropospheric scatter radio systems.

Laser Beams through Tubes and Rods

Military communications systems have to be mobile and flexible. Inter-city systems, on the other hand, depend on a permanent, fully reliable link to guide laser beams for long distances over hills and around bends. These systems will almost certainly use pipes of some kind to transmit the beam from place to place.

There are several ways in which electromagnetic waves can be guided through a pipe. In one, the wave is reflected back and forth between highly reflecting walls, following a zigzag path about the central line of the tube. Inert gas, which produces less corrosion than air, usually fills the tube. Provided that the gas and the wavelength are suitably chosen, the gas itself does not attenuate the waves, but there is always some loss at each reflection because of manufacturing imperfections in the walls. Guides of this kind are already used at microwave frequencies, but they will be much harder to make for use with light because, as a general rule, losses increase as the frequency increases.

The second type of guide consists of a solid insulating transparent rod. Again, the light follows a zigzag path (see the diagram below), with reflection taking place at the junction between the dielectric and the surrounding medium. Glass fibers are an example of this type of guide. Each fiber has a core of optical glass sheathed with another type of glass having a lower refractive index than the core. Total internal reflection takes place at the junction of the two glasses. Losses are fairly high, and glass fibers have only been used so far for transmitting laser beams over distances of a few meters. But they are very useful because they are mechanically very flexible and can be made so narrow that they will bend the light through large angles, as shown in the diagram at the bottom of page 85.

Light paths in different types of optical waveguide. Upper diagram: the path in a hollow metal tube or a solid insulating rod. Lower diagram: the path in a hollow tube with lenses.

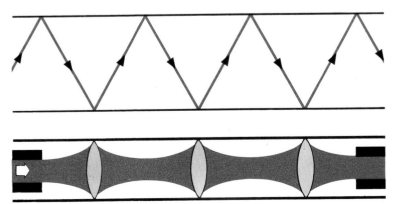

A third type of guide consists of a hollow tube where the beam, instead of being reflected from side to side, is kept on its path by a series of lenses placed at intervals down the tube. This is illustrated in the lower part of the diagram on page 83. An optical waveguide of this type has been built at the Army Electronic Command Laboratory in the United States. The attenuation for each kilometer of travel is only about a quarter of the amount acceptable in a long-distance microwave waveguide transmission system. Lenses about 100 meters apart will keep the beam within a 2-cm-diameter tube, but will not allow the beam to follow unexpected curves. There are two ways of getting around this snag: the position of the lenses can be adjusted by remote

Opposite: an experimental optical-beam waveguide consisting of a 6-cm-diameter aluminum pipe with lenses inside. This waveguide is of the type shown in the lower diagram on page 83.

Gas lenses in a hollow guide. The heating coils placed at intervals along the guide produce regions in which the gas near the walls is hotter than the gas in the center, giving the effect of a converging lens. The gas flows continuously through each section of the guide.

The paths of light rays in fiber optics. As long as a ray keeps striking the interface at a glancing angle it will not escape, so the narrow fiber optic is better than the wide one for guiding light around corners.

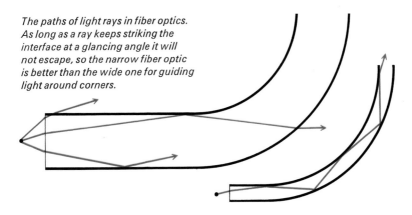

control to correct for any deviations from a straight path, or the distance between lenses can be made much shorter. A beam can be made to follow the curvature of a motorway, for example, by placing the lenses only a meter or so apart.

The pressure is kept slightly below normal atmospheric pressure in almost all hollow guides to reduce the effects of varying temperature gradients in the air inside the pipe. Since the refractive index of air depends upon its temperature, such variations would deflect the beam slightly and increase the losses.

Each lens will introduce some loss, and the spacing between lenses therefore has to be made as great as possible. Quartz optical lenses absorb laser wavelengths less than other types, but they have some residual surface roughness that causes considerable loss. Bell Telephone Laboratories have developed a *gas lens* that seems to get around this difficulty. It consists of a $\frac{1}{2}$-cm-diameter metal tube heated at intervals. Cool nitrogen or carbon dioxide gas is pumped continuously through the tube from one end to the other. Where the heaters are, the gas nearest the walls will reach a higher temperature than the gas in the center of the tube, and so will have a lower density and a lower refractive index. This change in the density of gas across the tube produces a converging-lens effect, which concentrates the beam along the axis of the tube. Gas lenses of this type, illustrated on page 85, cause almost no loss in the intensity of the light beam.

Laser Illumination

So far we have considered how lasers might be used to carry information between one point and another. But lasers can be used for other purposes within communications systems. One such application is as a light source for television systems, to illuminate the scene being televised.

The idea here is to dispense with the conventional light sources used in present-day television, which are very cumbersome. This does not mean simply replacing conventional light with laser light, because there is no general illumination of the scene by the laser. Instead, its narrow beam scans the scene rapidly from side to side and top to bottom, and the system works even if there is otherwise total darkness. Whatever the level of illumination,

A laser transmitter in the form of a small "pistol" sends out an infrared beam carrying the sounds spoken into the microphone. The beam is aimed at a lens like the one held by the man in the foreground, then demodulated and reconverted into sound by a loudspeaker. This experimental unit has operated over a 10-km. range between points of high ground in the United States.

the scene appears on the television screen as sharply and clearly as if it were in daylight.

The mechanics of the system developed by Robert S. Rowley of Perkin-Elmer Corporation, Norwalk, Connecticut, are rather similar to those used in the mechanical television systems developed in the 1920s and early 1930s. These systems were later superseded by all-electronic television systems; but now the advent of the laser makes them look attractive again, at least for some special purposes.

In the Perkin-Elmer system, the red beam from a continuous-wave helium-neon gas laser is directed onto a 16-sided polygonal rotating mirror. This mirror scans the beam backward and forward in the horizontal direction, and directs it onto a 24-sided polygonal drum that also rotates, moving the horizontal line scanned by the beam up and down, from top to bottom of the

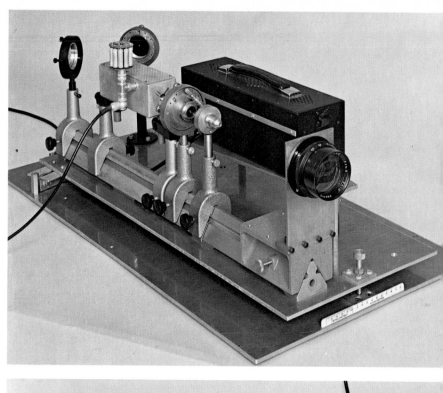

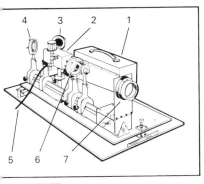

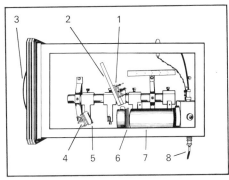

ANSMITTER

Laser (Helium-Neon)
Modulator
Plane Mirror
Plane Mirror

5. Modulator supply
6. Polarizer
7. Lens

RECEIVER

1. Mirror Adjustments
2. Plane Mirror
3. Lens
4. Mirror Adjustments

5. Plane Mirror
6. Narrow Band Filter
7. Photomultiplier
8. Photomultiplier Output

Opposite: an experimental laser television system, showing the transmitter (above) and receiver (below). The key to their working is at the top of this page. The signal comes in along the modulator supply wire, and the modulator uses the electrooptic effect in a crystal of ammonium dihydrogen phosphate (see diagram, page 72). The laser beam is collected by the lens in the receiver and demodulated by the photomultiplier, and the signal is carried away along the photomultiplier output wire.

Below: a laser television system being tested in the laboratory.

scene. The end result is that the beam scans an angle of 45° from left to right and 30° up and down, at a rate of 60 times a second. The system was designed to match closely the picture-quality standards of conventional American public television broadcasting.

The laser power transmitted to the scene, which is 15 milliwatts, is well below the level that would be dangerous to the eye. Indeed, it is almost impossible to see the beam when it is scanning rapidly backward and forward. The light reflected from the scene passes through an optical filter, which rejects all light on wavelengths other than that of the laser beam. This filter enables the system to be used for televising well-lit scenes as well as scenes in complete darkness. After passing through the filter, the light is picked up by a photomultiplier detector.

Unlike conventional television cameras, there is no need for a lens system to image the light coming from the scene. With an ordinary lighting system, light reflected from different objects in the scene would overlap inside the camera if no lens were used, but with the Perkin-Elmer system this does not happen. This means, for one thing, that the system has an infinite depth of focus—objects at any distance from the camera will produce sharp images. The only limitations encountered here are when looking at objects less than about 60 cm. from the camera, when parallax effects give trouble, and at very long ranges, when the returned light becomes too weak to be used. The first Perkin-Elmer system, which was described to the public toward the end of 1966, had a range of more than 9 meters. This could be extended to over 150 meters for strongly reflecting targets.

Another interesting result of having no lens is that light sources, such as an electric light bulb or the flame from a match, are not imaged. Their light simply spreads over the whole of the displayed picture and appears as an increase in the general brightness. Much of this "noise" is removed by the optical filter. The smoke from a cigarette lighter, for example, shows up quite clearly on the screen because it reflects the laser beam, while the flame of the lighter is invisible.

One obvious application for a system like this is as an unseen watcher of dark areas such as doorways. It is possible to detect people at distances of up to a mile in the dark with a special version of the system. Other possible applications include automatic reading of license number plates to catch traffic offenders, automatic billing for vehicles entering toll autoroutes or congested city centers, and all-weather landing for aircraft, on runways or helicopter landing spots marked off with reflective paints or tapes that reflect the beam hundreds of times as intensely as the surrounding ground does. The system would be particularly valuable in remote military bases in dense areas such as jungles. In fog conditions the system has proved much more sensitive, over distances of a few hundred meters, than conventional direct vision. It may also be possible to investigate the nocturnal habits of animals. In the television broadcasting field, the system is expected to prove very useful for news reporting because it can be set up at remote locations, to televise some hot news item, much more quickly than bulky conventional lighting equipment.

4 Holography

The ability to record and reproduce truly three-dimensional images has been much sought after by scientists and inventors. Early systems in which the viewer had to wear special spectacles led to something of a boom in 3D motion picture shows in the early 1950s, but this boom collapsed very quickly. The reason for the collapse may have been that producers tended to concentrate on stories giving full scope to trick effects, while audiences quickly got tired of dodging arrows and stones. More likely reasons, however, were the eyestrain caused by looking through the special spectacles at screens that were often poorly adjusted, and the nuisance of having to obtain and wear the spectacles. In any case the pictures, although they appeared three-dimensional, were not exactly like real three-dimensional scenes. It was impossible to look around an object in the foreground to see what was behind it. This can, of course, be done when viewing real scenes, and it can be done with the three-dimensional displays produced by *holography*, a new technique that makes use

The object in the girl's hand is a hologram—a photographic record of a
scene in the form of an interference
pattern made with laser light. The
hologram does not look anything like
the scene, but if it is illuminated by light
from the laser a three-dimensional
image of the scene appears.

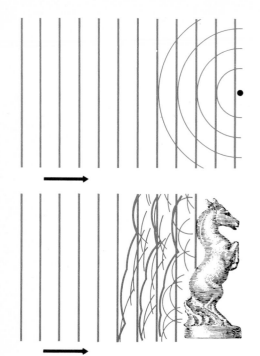

A point object illuminated by plane waves scatters light in a series of spherical waves (upper diagram). A real object behaves like a collection of point objects. Each point on the object's surface is the center of outgoing spherical waves, and the tangent to all of these is the wave front for the whole object (lower diagram).

of laser beams.

Three-dimensional large-screen holographic motion pictures are not likely to be commercially feasible for many years, if ever, but small-scale holographic displays of both still and moving scenes have already been produced in a number of laboratories around the world. Holographic television, although likely to be complex and expensive, is at least theoretically feasible and is likely to be used for special purposes in the not too distant future. Holography is already finding applications in industry, on the production line. As each fresh component comes off the line, it can be checked by placing it in the same position as a holographic display of a master component. Very little skill is needed by the operator, since any error in the fresh component shows up immediately.

How Holography Works

When we look at a scene, or take a photograph of it, a number of processes are taking place. Light from a source such as the sun or an electric lamp shines onto the objects in the scene and these objects reflect it in the manner illustrated above. The reflected light has some of the features of the objects impressed on it in various ways, such as the shapes of the wave fronts and variations in amplitude across each wave front. This information-carrying light enters our eyes, or a camera, and leaves an impression on the light-sensitive region (the retina or film) inside.

At their best, retinas and films can only record the *intensity* and *color* of the incident light, and the images on them are made up of variations in these two quantities. These images do not contain any information about the line-of-sight distance of an object. Such information is, of course, essential for a three-dimensional record. It is impossible to tell from a photograph how far away the objects in it are, and whether one of them is farther off than another, unless the objects happen to be familiar enough for us to judge this from their apparent sizes. The same is true of the image on the human retina; we can judge distances properly only because we have two eyes. Each eye views the scene from a different angle, and the brain is able to interpret this difference in terms of distance.

Intensity and color are not the only characteristics of the

When two sets of plane waves strike a photographic plate (left), constructive and destructive interference between them produces an image consisting of a series of equally spaced bright and dark fringes. The spacing of these fringes depends on the angle between the two beams. When the interference is between a set of plane waves and a set of spherical waves (right), the spacing between fringes increases down the plate, and each fringe is a circle instead of a straight line.

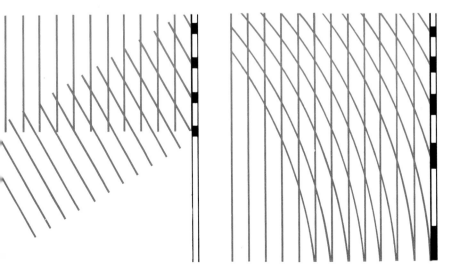

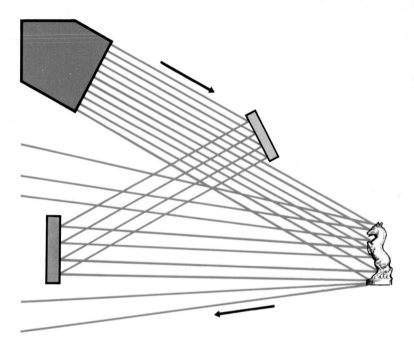

incident light, and one of the others—its phase—contains the information from which one could, in principle, deduce the distances we need for a truly three-dimensional record. To be more precise, this information is contained in the relative phases of the light waves striking different parts of the sensitive area at one moment. Films and retinas do not respond directly to such phase variations, but we can get a record of them by using the phenomenon of *interference*, which was explained in Chapter 1, and this is the technique used in holography. The principle is shown in the diagram on page 95. On the left is a plan view of two wave trains, of the same frequency and amplitude, reaching a photographic plate. The red bars represent the crests of the waves. The foremost crest of the first wave train—the wave train striking the plate head-on—has just reached the plate, and at certain points it coincides with crests from the second wave train —the one striking the plate at an angle. At these points of intersection the two sets of waves reinforce each other. At the intermediate points, on the other hand, the crests of set 1 coincide with the troughs of set 2, so the waves cancel each other out. The photographic plate will therefore show alternate regularly spaced light and dark fringes, and these fringes are a true record of the

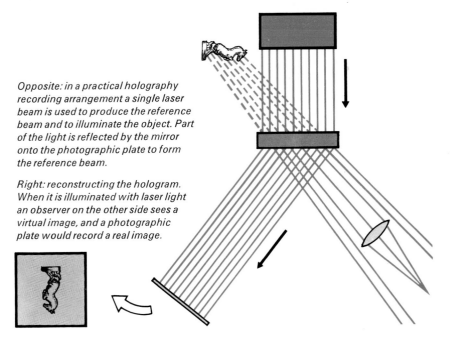

Opposite: in a practical holography recording arrangement a single laser beam is used to produce the reference beam and to illuminate the object. Part of the light is reflected by the mirror onto the photographic plate to form the reference beam.

Right: reconstructing the hologram. When it is illuminated with laser light an observer on the other side sees a virtual image, and a photographic plate would record a real image.

way in which the phase of the second wave train differs from the first.

In this example, both sets of waves are plane waves—that is, each one represents a parallel-sided light beam moving in a fixed direction. Suppose now that the shape of the wave fronts in set 2 is changed from plane to spherical, as shown in the right-hand diagram on page 95. (In terms of water waves, the analogous waves are those produced by a stone dropping into a pool. Each wave crest spreads outward in a circle.) The fringes produced in this case are circular, and the spacing decreases away from the center. The difference between the patterns produced on the photographic plate in the two cases illustrated on page 95 is characteristic of the difference between the second set of waves in each case. If we regard the first set—the plane waves traveling at right angles to the plate—as a *reference beam*, the pattern on the photographic plate contains all the information needed in principle to reconstruct the second set, which we shall refer to in future as the *signal beam* (even though it is not always, strictly speaking, a beam, but may be a set of spherical waves, as in one of the examples we have just discussed). Any information in the signal beam is, therefore, contained in the pattern too.

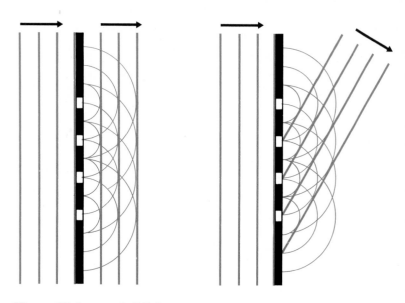

How a Hologram is Made

This is the principle of holography, and the diagram on page 96 illustrates how it is applied in practice to make a three-dimensional record of a chess piece. A laser beam is used, one half of it—the reference beam—being reflected by a plane mirror directly onto a photographic plate, and the other half—the signal beam—being reflected by the chess piece onto the same photographic plate. The result is an interference pattern on the plate that is a precise record, in coded form, of the signal beam. Such a record is called a *hologram*. The hologram does not look anything like an ordinary photograph of a chess piece, but it contains information not only about the intensity variations in the signal beam (as an ordinary photograph would) but also about the phase variations. The wave fronts in the signal beam are neither plane nor spherical, but have the rather complicated shapes shown on page 94, reflecting the shape of the chess piece. The amplitude varies over the surface of each wave front according to the amount of light reflected by different parts of the object toward the plate. The pattern on the plate will be correspondingly complicated. An example of such a pattern is shown opposite.

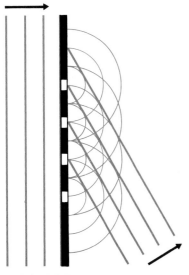

When a hologram is illuminated with laser light it acts as a diffraction grating. If it consists of equally spaced fringes, a zero-order diffracted beam emerges traveling straight on (far left), and two first-order beams emerge traveling at equal angles to the zero-order beam.

Below: details of a hologram of fog particles. Usually, holograms contain circular patterns due to extraneous dust particles, the true holographic record of the object being too small to be visible, but the circles in this photograph are due to the fog particles themselves.

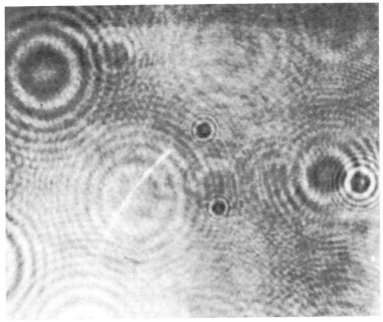

Left: a reconstructed hologram. This photograph of champagne pouring into a glass was made by placing the photographic plate in front of a hologram that was then illuminated by a laser.

Opposite: illuminating a hologram consisting of unequally spaced circular fringes (see diagram on page 95). The first-order wave fronts emerging are spherical, one converging to form a real image, the other diverging as if from a virtual image.

Reconstructing the Image

How do we decode the complicated-looking message on the hologram? The answer is surprisingly simple: just shine a laser beam through it from the same direction as the original reference beam. An observer looking through the hologram from the other side will see the chess piece and any other objects that were with it (see the diagram on page 97), and if he moves his head sideways he will observe the parallax effect characteristic of truly three-dimensional images. In fact, there are two images of the chess piece produced, not just one: a photographic plate in front of the hologram, in the position shown in the diagram, will record a picture of the chess piece without the need for any lenses.

This reconstruction of the image takes place through the phenomenon of diffraction, which was explained in Chapter 1. When the illuminating beam from the laser strikes the hologram, the dark areas on the hologram block light altogether while the clear areas allow light through. The light that is able to squeeze through any one of these clear gaps is diffracted. It spreads out in all directions as it leaves the hologram, immediately meets light spreading out from neighboring gaps, and interferes with it. The result of this combined diffraction and interference is that beams travel out from the hologram in certain directions

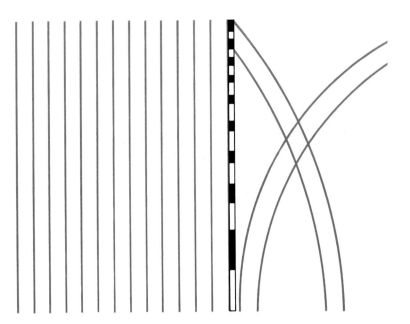

but not in others. One of these beams is a reconstructed version of the original signal beam used in making the hologram. It travels out in the same direction, relative to the hologram, and its wave fronts are just like those in the signal beam. If an observer is looking at the hologram from this direction he will see just what he would have seen if the signal beam had entered his eye —that is, a three-dimensional view of the chess piece. What has happened, in effect, is that the waves reflected from the chess piece and spreading out from it were "frozen" in position by the holographic recording process, and are released and allowed to travel on by the reproducing process.

Reconstructing Two Simple Holograms

Let us look at the reconstruction process in more detail for the two simple holograms whose construction processes are shown in the diagram on page 95. For the first one, the signal beam and the reference beam are both plane waves, and the hologram consists of a series of straight parallel fringes. If we illuminate it with a plane wave coming at right angles to it—just like the original reference beam in the diagram—diffraction will take place, as shown in a simplified way in the sequence of diagrams on pages 98–99.

Each opening in the hologram can be regarded as the source of approximately cylindrical waves. The first diagram shows that these reinforce each other in the forward direction, producing a plane wave—the zero-order diffracted wave—that is simply an attenuated version of the illuminating beam. This zero-order beam is not part of the holographic image. However, the other diagrams show that there are two more directions in which reinforcement occurs and a plane wave comes out. The waves emerging in these directions are the first-order diffracted waves. One of these is traveling at precisely the same angle to the illuminating beam as the original signal beam was to the reference beam. The angle at which the diffracted beam leaves the hologram depends on the distance between the fringes in the hologram, and this, in turn, depends on the angle between the original reference beam and the signal beam. The result is an outgoing beam just like the original signal beam. The other first-order beam, called the *ghost beam*, is also traveling at the same angle to the illuminating beam, but on the other side of it. At larger angles, there are higher-order diffracted waves which are of relatively low intensity and are not shown.

The second hologram whose production is shown on page 95 is made using a set of spherical waves as the signal beam, and the reconstruction process is shown on page 101. Again, there is an emerging plane wave that is an attenuated version of the illuminating beam, produced by the zero-order diffraction process. This plane wave is not shown in the diagram. The two first-order beams are shown, however. Because the spacing between fringes increases down the hologram, and the fringes themselves are circular, the wave fronts of these first-order beams are spherical.

Equipment used to make a hologram. The photographic plate (the hologram) is at bottom center, just below the chessboard. The beam (from a gas laser) enters at top right and part of it (the reference beam) is reflected at top left directly onto the plate. The rest is reflected at two partially reflecting plates and reflected again, by the two mirrors at the bottom, onto the chessmen, which are thus illuminated from two angles. The rather complicated paths are meant to keep the optical path lengths of the signal beam and the reference beam approximately equal to each other. Gas lasers have a coherence length of a few meters, and the paths must not differ by more than this.

These three photographs were made from the hologram whose production is shown on page 103. The different positions of the chessmen relative to one another illustrate the parallax effect observed by someone viewing the illuminated hologram and moving his head sideways. The parallax effect is characteristic of three-dimensional scenes.

One of them is a replica of the original signal beam; the other, the ghost beam, is also similar except that the wave fronts have opposite curvature to the wave fronts in the signal beam. The first beam is spreading outward as though it originated from the source of the original signal beam; the ghost beam is converging toward a point in front of the hologram. This difference between the two first-order beams is not apparent in the diagram on page 99 because the case illustrated there was the rather special one where the signal and reference beams were both plane waves.

In all other cases, the two first-order beams produce different kinds of image, as shown on page 97 for the case of the chess piece. One is a virtual image (this is the type of image produced by an ordinary plane mirror, in which light rays entering the eye appear to be diverging from a point that is not, in fact, reached

Opposite, top: even though only a small area of the hologram is illuminated, the entire original scene is reconstructed. The other two photographs show that as the area of the illuminating beam (shown at the bottom of each photograph) is increased, the definition of the image improves but the depth of focus decreases.

by the light at all). The other, formed by the ghost beam, is a real image and can be recorded directly on a photographic plate, as stated on page 100.

The Holographic Image

Holograms have several interesting properties. The image produced by a hologram is genuinely three-dimensional, and shows the parallax effect—if the observer moves his head sideways, objects at unequal distances appear to move relative to one another. It is possible to look around an object and see what is behind it. This three-dimensional nature of the images is shown in the photographs on pages 104–105. We cannot say of a hologram, as we can of an ordinary photograph, that any one part of it corresponds to a particular part of the image; the entire image is on every small area of the hologram (although looking through different areas gives differently angled views), so if the photographic plate containing the hologram is broken the image can still be reconstructed from one of the pieces. The only disadvantage would be that the small area of the hologram would lead to poor resolution in the image. This is shown on pages 106–107, as is another important feature of holograms—although the resolution of the image gets worse as the effective area of the hologram is reduced, the depth of focus of the image increases.

When a hologram is made, and when it is displayed, laser beams are aimed at it from particular angles only. If a photographic plate has had one hologram recorded on it, it can be used again to record a quite different scene, provided that the light is beamed at it from a different angle. In other words, several holograms can be stored simultaneously on one photographic plate. To display a particular image, the plate is illuminated from the same angle as was used in making the hologram of that image.

This ability to store several images rather than just one is another respect in which the hologram is superior to an ordinary photograph, and suggests that an important application of holography will be in the storage of information, because the density of information that can be stored in a hologram is so very high. Holography would also be useful in this field for another reason, connected with the fact that any one part of a hologram contains the complete image. When records are stored on microfilm, a small scratch on the film may delete a lot of information—several lines of text, for example. If the microfilm was of a hologram, it would always be possible to extract the information as long as some part of it was undamaged.

It is a curious fact that holography, or *wave-front reconstruction* as it is sometimes called, was invented in 1947, several years before the laser. The inventor was Professor Dennis Gabor of London University, who hoped to use the technique to improve the resolution of electron microscopes. According to the quantum theory, moving electrons have probability waves associated with them, and holograms can be made with these just as with light waves. As things turned out, Gabor was overtaken by other

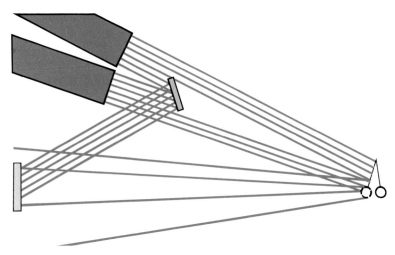

To make a hologram of a moving object the angle of the laser beam is changed after each exposure and the successive images are recorded on a single hologram.

technical developments that did more for electron microscopes than holography could, and the technique fell into disuse during the 1950s. Its full exploitation had to wait for the laser to provide intense beams of coherent light.

Moving Images

Recording and displaying moving objects by holography presents a number of serious problems, but simple animated holograms have been demonstrated by Professor E. N. Leith and his colleagues at the University of Michigan, where a great deal of work on holography has been done under the leadership of Professor G. W. Stroke.

One could make an animated hologram in the same way as one makes an ordinary motion picture, using a separate frame for each hologram. Leith preferred to take advantage of the fact that several holograms can be stored on one photographic plate. He recorded a series of images of a slowly moving object on a single plate by altering the angle between the reference beam and the plate after each exposure, as shown above. To reproduce the moving images he illuminated the plate with laser light from each of the angles used in the recording process in turn. The result was a series of images that, when produced at a high enough rate, gave a flicker-free display of the original moving object. So far only very simple images, such as those of a swinging pendulum and a moving toy duck, have been produced in this way, because very costly equipment is required and the process takes a very long time; but there is undoubtedly great scope for development here.

One of the problems is that the object must not move appreciably during the exposure time. To be more precise, movement during this period must be kept down to a fraction of a wavelength of light. It is easy to see why; the nature of the holographic recording process is such that if one of the two light beams moves half a wavelength nearer to the plate, the hologram will be completely smudged. The wavelength of light is roughly 5000 A., or less than 1 thousandth of a millimeter, and movement must be kept well below this amount. This means that the laser used must be capable of being switched on and off very fast, and must supply enough light during this very short time to illuminate the scene properly. The parallel development, since about 1965, of very fast shutters based on the electrooptic effect (see page 71) and of very high-power lasers means that we can now switch on a sufficiently powerful laser beam for less than one hundred-millionth of a second. In this time a man walking at normal speed would move about 200 angstrom units, so it would certainly be possible to produce a motion picture of a person walking with such a laser, but it might be difficult to show anything faster than this.

The Michigan group have produced holograms about one foot square, which several people can view. Unfortunately, it is going to be very difficult to produce hologram plates as large as a cinema screen, and the projection problems also seem to be very serious. Projecting holographic images is far more complicated than projecting an ordinary two-dimensional motion picture, because the lens system must magnify equally in the lateral and axial dimensions (along the line of sight as well as perpendicular to it) if there is to be no distortion of the three-dimensional scene displayed. Unfortunately no known optical system has this property, so the problem of projecting three-dimensional hologram images to a large audience is a formidable one, which may take a long time to solve. Nevertheless, three-dimensional hologram movies for viewing by limited audiences are undoubtedly a practical possibility.

Holographic Television

Holographic television is theoretically possible, though it has not yet been achieved in practice. Televising a scene requires very high levels of illumination, higher than those used for ordinary film-making, and the scene would probably have to be illuminated with several lasers to provide such high levels without harsh effects, and to illuminate the scene from different directions. A separate laser time-locked to the illuminating lasers can be used for the reference beam. A television camera of fairly standard design could convert the hologram produced on its photosensitive surface into electrical signals suitable for modulating a television transmitter. The most difficult part of a holographic television system would be reproducing the hologram in the receiver. Once it had been reproduced, the hologram could be illuminated with laser light to reproduce the scene in exactly the same way as other holograms are reproduced. In early 1967 there appeared to be two techniques that might, after suitable development, be used to reproduce the hologram.

One of them, the Fischer system, was developed as a method of showing television pictures on a large theater screen. Professor Fritz Fischer took out the original patent in 1940. The heart of the system is an oil layer of minute thickness called the *Eidophor liquid*, on either side of which is a screen with slits in it. The slits are arranged so that the second set normally blocks any light that has passed through the first set. However, if the Eidophor liquid is deformed in some way, it will affect light passing through it and allow some, at least, to pass through both sets of slits. Distortion of the liquid can be achieved by scanning across it with a beam of electrons modulated by the incoming signal; these produce varying electric charges on the film, corresponding to the variations in the interference pattern on the original hologram. These electric charges cause minute corrugations in the film, which in turn diffract light passing through it. If this light comes from a laser in the television receiver and is aimed at the correct angle (corresponding to the direction of the reference beam in the camera) the light emerging from the system will be a reconstructed signal beam, just as with the standard holographic reconstruction process.

An alternative arrangement would be to use one of the newly developed photochromic glasses. These types of glass are sensitive to light—when exposed to bright light they darken and remain dark until the light is switched off again, when they clear gradually. The beam produced by a laser in the receiver is modulated by the incoming signal and focused onto a sheet of photochromic glass, which it scans from side to side and top to bottom, producing a light-and-dark pattern corresponding to the pattern on the hologram. The glass is then illuminated by another laser beam, which emerges as a reconstructed signal beam.

There is still some doubt about the timetable for the development of practical holographic television systems, but little doubt that they will eventually be possible. Gabor and Stroke, among others, feel that it is beyond the present state of the art. But this is a field in which the amount of money available for research and development is a key factor in determining the speed with which practical equipment becomes available, and several people in the United States think that the economic returns from a successful holographic television system would be so great that it is worth making a real start. One senior executive of an American electronics company felt strongly enough about it to resign because the company did not back the idea.

Holographic Measurement

A group of engineers working with Leith at the University of Michigan has concentrated on applying holography to the practical problems of measurement that occur on the production line and in the research laboratory. They have been most in-

A holographic interferogram of the shock waves produced by a .22-caliber bullet traveling through air at 1000 meters per second.

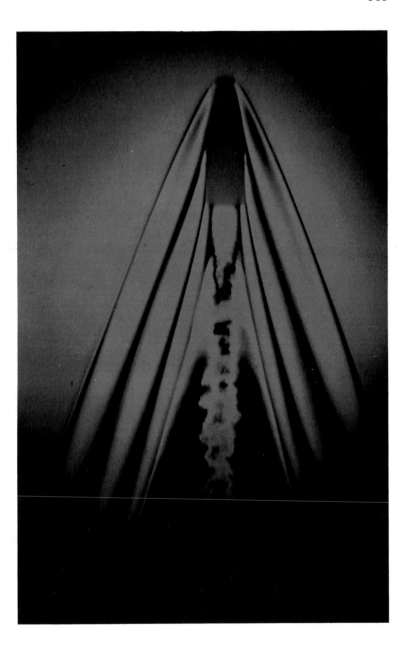

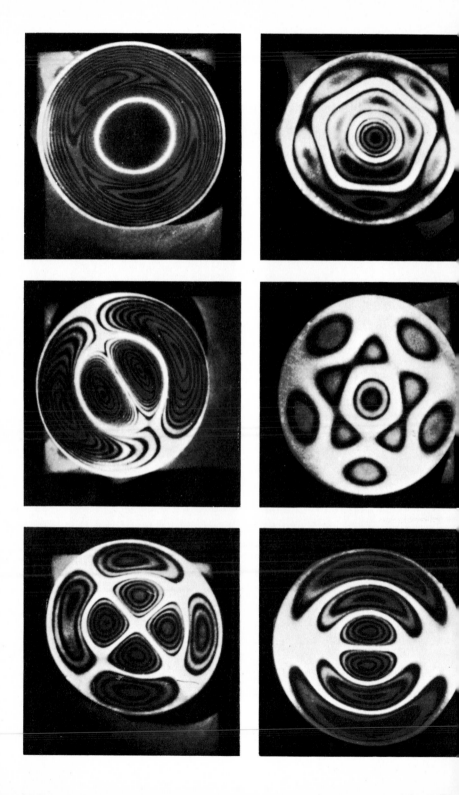

terested in ways of measuring vibrations and small deformations —vibrations of aircraft components and deformations of metal under strain, for example. A hologram of the object on which measurements are being made is first produced. The hologram is then illuminated with laser light so that the reconstructed wave fronts appear to be coming from an object in exactly the same place as the real object. Thus, the holographic image is superimposed upon the object, and light reflected from the object can interfere with the light apparently coming from the image. Even the most minute difference in size or shape between object and

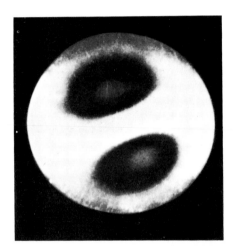

Holographic interferometry is used to analyze vibrations. These interferograms show the bottom of a 35-mm. film can vibrating in several different modes.

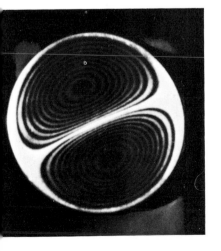

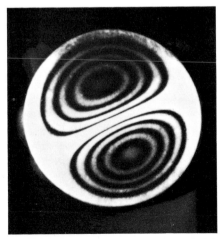

image will produce an interference pattern, and slight changes in the shape of the object will show up immediately as changes in the interference pattern. This technique will detect changes in size less than a wavelength of light. Pictures of stress concentrations can be obtained by testing components in tension or compression. Welds and flaws in the walls of hollow vessels can be exposed by heating the air inside the vessel and observing the minute variations in the expansion of the walls. Pressure vessels can be tested in a similar way, since any weak spots would expand to a slightly greater extent than the surrounding areas when the vessel was pressurized. Examples of holographic interferometry are shown in the photographs on pages 113–115.

Instead of superimposing the reconstructed image on the object itself, we could compare the images produced by two holograms of the object—one made before and one after the change that is being studied. By doing this we lose the advantage of continuous observation but may gain in other respects. For instance, the object itself may be vibrating but it may be some other change, and not the extraneous vibrations, that we wish to observe. Another possibility is that the change is taking place too fast for continuous observation, in which case using a hologram in place of the object itself gives the same advantage as ordinary high-speed photography.

Even better is to use the same photographic plate for both holograms. There is then no need to ensure that the laser wavelength and the optical arrangements used when viewing the interference pattern are exactly the same as those used for recording it. Any distortion of the emulsion or change in the optical system affects both holograms to the same degree and does not alter the interference pattern. This would not be so when using a separate photographic plate for each hologram. It is even possible to use an entirely different laser for viewing. Rapidly changing objects can be recorded by using a single half-microsecond pulse from a ruby laser, and studied at leisure by illuminating the hologram with the beam from a continuous-wave gas laser.

A fly's-eye lens produces hundreds of images of an object, each from a slightly different angle. The compound photograph can be used, together with a laser beam, to make a hologram.

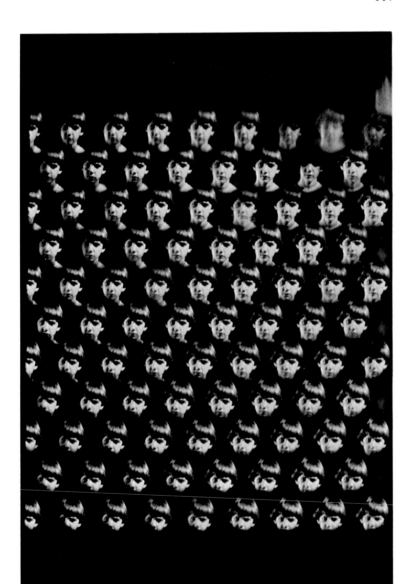

Displaying and Recording without a Laser

Lasers are quite expensive devices and the use of holography, particularly by the amateur, would be greatly increased if the laser could be relegated to a laboratory in the same way as most photographic developing and printing equipment is relegated to the laboratory.

Holograms recorded in laser light can be reproduced by white light from the sun or a conventional light source in several ways, one of which was developed by C. B. Burckhardt of the Bell Telephone Company. The hologram is illuminated by white light. All the light is bent by the interference pattern, but the amount of bending depends upon the wavelength of the light, so the white light is split up into a series of spaced, differently colored images on the far side of the hologram. The light then passes through a second hologram of a special type. The function of this s˜cond hologram is not to distort the waves, but simply to bend them back again and recombine the differently colored images. The result is a three-dimensional black-and-white image of the object used in making the first hologram.

Another method of white-light illumination, developed by Stroke and the Michigan group, produces a single-color image. The hologram, which is on a thick photographic plate, is made in monochromatic light from a laser in the usual way except that the reference beam is directed at the *back* of the plate. In an ordinary hologram, recorded on an emulsion of finite thickness, the fringes are really layers that extend in depth through the emulsion. Viewed edge-on, the layers are at right angles to the front and back of the plate. Using the thick-hologram method of Stroke, however, the hologram pattern consists of layers parallel to the front and back of the plate, not perpendicular to it. When the hologram is illuminated with white light these layers reflect back to the observer only light on the same wavelength as was used in the recording process. This method could be extended to make multicolor images by using lasers of different colors to record the hologram and illuminating it with white light as just described.

Robert V. Pole, of the IBM research center in New York, has developed a camera for taking films—in ordinary light—that can later be processed with a laser to produce a hologram of the original scene. The lens in this camera is a *fly's-eye lens*, which, as its name implies, consists of many separate lenses each projecting a slightly differently angled view of the scene onto the photographic medium at the back of the camera. An array of tiny images of the scene, each taken from a slightly different angle, is thus produced on the photographic negative (see the photograph on page 117). If such a negative, after development, is illuminated by laser light and placed in front of a second fly's eye lens, the light waves on the far side of the lens are similar to those coming from the original scene.

These light waves impinge on a second photographic plate and interfere with a laser reference beam in the usual manner. An interference pattern—that is, a hologram—is produced. It is a true hologram, which, when illuminated, produces a three-dimensional image.

Holography is still at a very early stage and, like the laser itself, the full scope of its applications can still be seen only very dimly. Nevertheless, it is likely to have a very important impact in the next decade and the prospects of the amateur photographer being able to shoot a roll of holograms in much the same way as today he shoots a roll of film are very real.

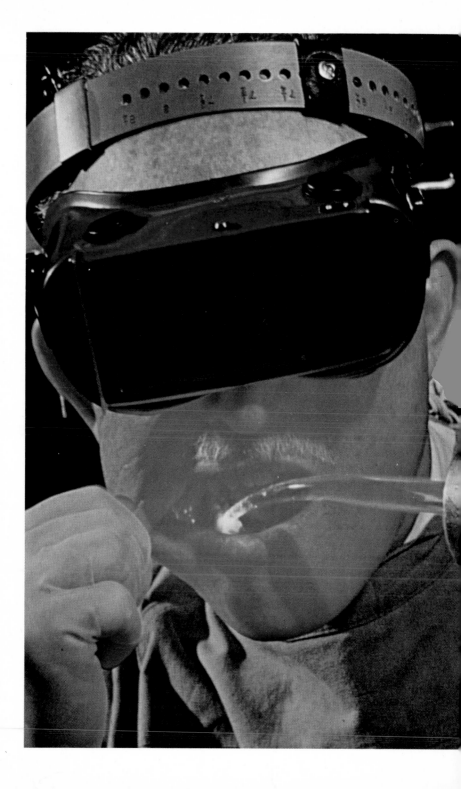

5 Lasers in Medicine

Ruby lasers have already been used to perform eye surgery on many thousands of people, and argon ion lasers are in use as high-precision scalpels for other surgical operations. Indeed, the practical use of lasers has probably been carried further in the field of medicine than in any other field. The very narrow laser beam is especially useful for performing operations on small, precisely defined areas, but it is not likely to be used for treating diseases that produce widespread disturbances in the body.

The eye is a fairly obvious organ on which to try out a laser because the transparent outer regions allow light of suitable wavelengths to pass through to the tissues at the back. These absorb laser light heavily and can therefore be destroyed or welded. Rather surprisingly the skin itself, the underlying fat, and much of the connective tissue within the body, such as muscle, are fairly transparent to laser beams of suitable wavelengths. Beams of quite high power will pass through such layers and then destroy tissue—such as cancer tumors—that absorbs laser light,

Laser beams can destroy decayed areas of teeth without affecting the surrounding healthy areas. Each pulse lasts only a thousandth of a second and the patient feels no pain.

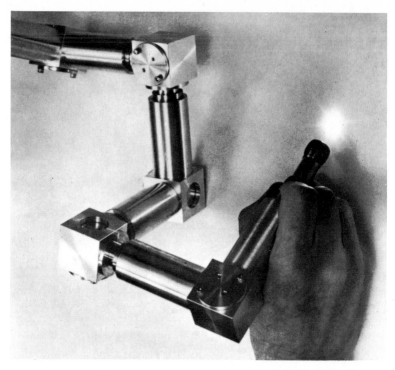

A "light knife" designed to be used as a scalpel. The hollow, jointed arm can be moved in any direction, and laser light is guided through it by prisms mounted in the corner cubes.

either naturally or because it has been artificially induced to absorb it. Surface skin growths are particularly easy to treat with a laser because they are usually much more absorbent than the surrounding healthy tissue, and a number of skin growths ranging from the common wart to some highly malignant cancers have been treated in the last few years. Laser beams can be transmitted through flexible fiber-optic waveguides to reach cancerous growths deep inside the body, and surgeons are particularly interested in the possibility of using lasers in this way for eradicating growths in the bladder, the lungs, the intestines, and the urogenital system. The great advantage of laser beams guided by fiber optics is that the site of the growth does not have to be opened up.

Lasers are also beginning to be used as diagnostic tools. If light from a helium-neon gas laser illuminates a specimen of tissue taken from the body, and the tissue is examined through a microscope, numerous bright and dark interference fringes appear. These fringes indicate minute differences in the thickness of the tissues—differences of about one wavelength of light—and this technique provides an accurate way of measuring the progress of very slow changes in the tissue. High-power pulsed laser beams are being used to vaporize tissue, as in the photograph on page 124. The vapor can be analyzed by conventional instruments, and from this analysis the condition of the tissue and the presence or absence of disease can be determined.

An end to the pain associated with a visit to the dentist may also be in sight. A laser beam can destroy the decayed areas of a tooth in a fraction of a second without causing pain to the patient. Lasers may also be useful in preventing dental decay because they can fuse over the small fissures in the enamel of a tooth that are the sites where decay usually starts.

Eye Surgery

To understand how the laser is used in eye surgery, let us take a look at the construction of the human eye, illustrated on page 125. It is a roughly spherical structure with a fairly thick outer wall. About one fifth of the outer wall of the eye, the *cornea*, is transparent, and behind it is the *anterior chamber*; this contains the *iris*, which opens and closes to control the amount of light entering the eye. The *lens*, which is encapsulated and attached to the inner walls of the eye, separates this anterior chamber from the *posterior chamber* of the eye. The anterior chamber is filled with a transparent liquid, the *aqueous humor*, which is being continuously changed and which feeds the cells in the cornea. The posterior chamber is filled with a transparent gel-like substance known as the *vitreous humor*.

The wall of the posterior chamber supports the *retina*, which plays a role like that of the film in a camera. It consists of a number of transparent layers in front of an opaque layer. The retina converts the light into electrical signals, which are transmitted along the optic nerve to the brain.

If any of the retinal layers are split, or detached from the underlying tissue, the path of the nerve impulses to the brain is interrupted and the affected area becomes blind. This is a

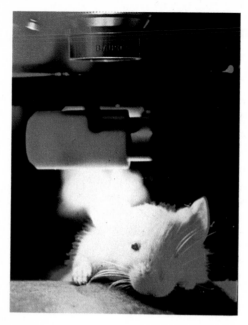

Left: a laser beam vaporizes a small amount of tissue from a mouse's ear. Spectroscopic analysis of the vapor may reveal particular diseases. A large amount of calcium, for instance, would lead to suspicion of cancer. The mouse is anesthetized and the laser beam does not harm it.

Opposite: the human eye. The color photograph below shows part of a retina, with whitish spots indicating laser-made welds. Each weld is actually about as big as a period on this page. There is a detachment in the top left-hand corner, where the picture is slightly out of focus. The photograph at the bottom shows a weld in cross section. The detached retina is the dark layer highest up in the picture. The choroid is below this, appearing light in the photograph, and the grayish-looking strip farther down is the sclerotic.

fairly common condition, which can be caused by some diseases or by a severe blow. It has been treated in the past by a wide range of different techniques for flattening the detached portions back against the wall of the eyeball and fixing them firmly. When this was not possible, the detached area was sealed off to prevent the whole retina from progressively peeling away and producing complete blindness.

Both the older techniques and the laser-based techniques work by producing localized heating or irritation (or both) of the retina and underlying tissue to form a small scar. Diathermy needles and probes cooled by solid carbon dioxide or solid nitrogen have been used, and so has the light from a powerful arc discharge lamp. The laser beam scores over these earlier methods in two ways. First, it can be focused to an extremely small spot, so that each weld is much smaller. This is particularly important when the detachment is in the central part of the retina—the part used for seeing fine detail. Second, welds can be made in a fraction of a second. The time taken is so short that the patient cannot blink and there is no need to clamp the eye in position. Very little heat and no pain are produced, so the patient does not need to be anesthetized. Two photographs of welds produced by lasers appear on the page opposite.

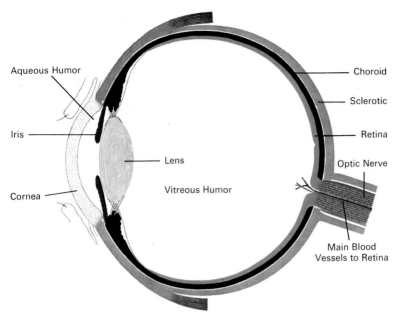

Aqueous Humor

Iris

Cornea

Choroid

Sclerotic

Retina

Lens

Vitreous Humor

Optic Nerve

Main Blood
Vessels to Retina

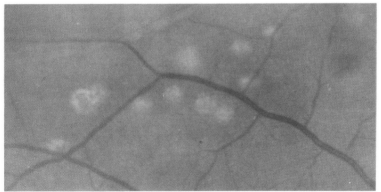

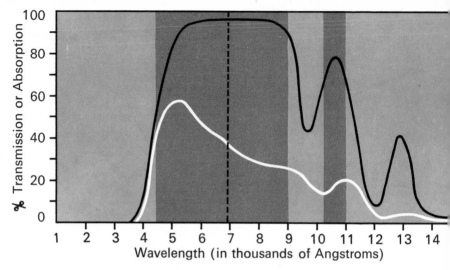

The transmission of different wavelengths by the optical system of the eye (black line) and their absorption by the retina (white line). The best wavelength to use is one where both curves have high values, indicated by the deep red. The vertical dashed line marks 6943 A., the wavelength of the ruby laser.

The wavelength used must be one that is transmitted by the cornea, the lens, and the aqueous and vitreous humors. The graphs on this page show that light whose wavelength is between 4500 and 9000 A., or around 10,600 A., passes through these areas with very little attenuation. The wavelength must also be one that is absorbed by the pigmented underlying tissue at the back of the retina. The graphs show that all wavelengths between 4000 and 12,000 A. are absorbed to some extent, with peak absorption occurring on a wavelength of about 5000 A. There are several different types of laser that emit light of suitable wavelengths, but the ruby laser produces the best wavelength, 6943 A. Helium-neon lasers emit light at 6328 A., but they may also emit infrared rays, which must be suppressed in some way, or they would be absorbed by the cornea or lens and cause serious damage to these tissues. The neodymium-in-glass lasers might be useful, because they emit on a wavelength of 10,600 A., but this wavelength is more easily absorbed by the lens of the eye than is the ruby-laser beam, so there would be risk of cataracts developing.

The laser ophthalmoscope shown in the diagram and photographs opposite was developed by the International Research and Development Company of Newcastle-on-Tyne, England, in

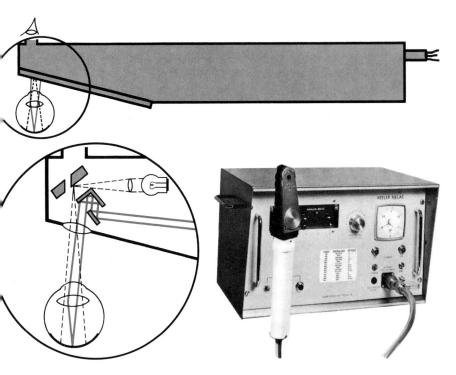

Above: the laser ophthalmoscope. The circular enlargement shows the path of the laser light (red) and that of the conventional light used by the surgeon for viewing the retina. The laser is in the handle of the instrument, which is attached by a cable to the external power supply.

Below: the laser ophthalmoscope in use.

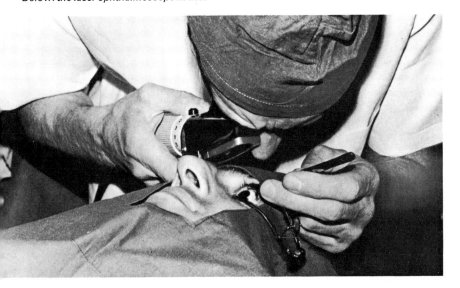

collaboration with the ophthalmic surgeon, H. Vernon Ingram. It contains a two-inch-long ruby crystal, which is pumped by a xenon flashtube in the handle of the instrument. A short (8 ten-thousandths of a second) pulse is used. A focusing device illuminates the retina and allows the surgeon to point the instrument accurately at the spot to be welded before firing the laser. The diameter of the laser beam is reduced from 0.64 to 0.32 cm. by a telescopic system to ensure that the whole beam passes through the patient's pupil, and it is reduced further by the focusing properties of the cornea and the lens.

Experiments on animals have shown that the smallest recognizable scar requires an energy of 0.008 joules to produce and that increasing the power causes the scars to increase in diameter. The smallest spot likely to be of practical use is about 0.1 mm. in diameter. Such a scar can be produced with an energy output of about 0.11 joules.

Protecting the Eye

In the early days of laser research a number of accidents occurred in American laboratories resulting in injuries to the eye. Scars and bubbles of gas can be produced as the result of disruption of the organic tissue in the eye by a laser beam. Cataracts have been started when the lens of the eye has absorbed energy of the wrong wavelength, or when the power has been too high. Damage to the cornea has also been produced.

One of the most serious aspects of the problem is that damage is caused instantaneously, and the researcher himself may not be aware that it is occurring. The degree of damage depends on the energy density and the length of exposure. The latter may be very short when a pulsed laser is used—perhaps 5 ten-thousandths of a second—but the former is often very high. If all the energy from a conventional ruby laser were to enter the eye, it would produce an energy density many hundreds of times that needed to produce the scars used in detached-retina operations, and about 47,000 times as great as the energy density the sun would produce in the same time.

It is common practice now for anybody working with lasers to wear safety glasses to protect his eyes. Even these are not safe in laboratories where laser energy is being converted to different wavelengths (by methods described in Chapter 7), and governments have issued rigid safety codes, designed to prevent damage to the skin as well as the eye, for laser laboratories.

Lasers in Dentistry

Dr. Leon Goldman and three of his colleagues at the Children's Hospital Research Foundation, Cincinnati, have used a ruby-laser beam focused onto the decayed cavities of a tooth to produce extensive destruction of the carious areas (see the photograph on page 120). The laser beam seems ideally suited to this purpose. It has a high energy density; it can be focused and directed onto a small area; and its energy is absorbed by the dark, decayed parts of the tooth but not by the healthy areas. Pulses only about 1 thousandth of a second long are enough to destroy the decayed areas, which gives the same sort of advantage to the patient as does the use of the laser for attaching retinas. There is no overall heating of the tooth because the pulse is so short, and there is none of the vibration produced by mechanical drills, so it seems likely that "drilling" with lasers can be carried out without the need for an anesthetic. Large, deep decayed areas can be drilled out by repeated firings of the laser, and cavities in inaccessible areas on the backs of teeth can be treated by transmitting the laser beam through a flexible glass-fiber rod.

Work is being done at Cincinnati and other places on the use of the laser to prevent tooth decay (as opposed to curing it). It is thought that decay starts in minute cracks in the surface of the enamel, which allow the decay-forming organisms to enter and reach the more sensitive areas. A laser beam might seal a crack by fusing the enamel on each side. It may also be possible to use new longer-lasting filling materials for teeth because a laser beam can melt highly refractory materials such as porcelain so that they can be used to fill in tooth cavities.

Lasers and the Skin

Very little reaction is produced in the normal skin of a white person by quite high doses of laser energy. Even with dark skins, which are somewhat more susceptible, the effect is not very marked. D. Smart, of International Research and Development, has pointed out that the threshold for observable effects on white skin or fatty tissue is about 25 joules per square centimeter for a ruby-laser beam. Significant effects start to take place once this level is passed, and eventually individual cells are destroyed. The various types of colored "spots" on the skin are much more susceptible to laser energy, and a laser beam whose energy is less than 25 joules per square centimeter can destroy such spots without affecting the surrounding skin. The common "old-lady brown spots" have been treated, tattoos and birth marks have been successfully removed, and, most important, many skin cancers have been partially or completely cured.

A highly malignant tumor about three centimeters across, in the cheek of a man who was one of Dr. Goldman's patients, was treated with nine bursts of laser energy. About 10 days later the tumor had disintegrated, and after six weeks the area was completely healed. Another patient, a woman, had about 60 secondary deposits from a main tumor—a case particularly suited to treatment by laser beams. Each deposit received a dose of energy from a ruby laser. The growths began to disappear after a week, and there had been no recurrence of the disease after 13 months. The photograph at the top of page 133 shows a laser being used to treat cancer on a patient's legs.

Other workers have been trying out high-energy ruby-laser beams on human tumors transplanted into the cheek pouches of hamsters. One surprising result was that the laser beam destroyed even some transparent tumors, such as cancer of the thyroid, which do not absorb laser energy. Another unexpected, and possibly very important, discovery was made by Dr. Paul E. McGuff at the New England Medical Center. After firing bursts of laser energy at a tumor in the cheek pouch of a hamster he found that a control tumor—one used for comparison, which had not been subjected to the laser energy—also disappeared. Dr. Goldman and his colleagues have observed similar reactions in distant parts of the body after a tumor has been treated, and Dr. Goldman has suggested as an explanation that antibodies may be produced by the destruction of tissue with a laser beam.

Unfortunately, not all types of skin cancer are sensitive to the radiation from a ruby laser. Of the 20 types known, only seven can be treated in this way, although beams of different wavelengths may prove to be more effective in treating some of the other 13 types. We may also find dyes that are selectively absorbed by malignant growths. If this can be done in such a way that the growth absorbs the laser energy more strongly, it will be possible to destroy it with beams of quite low energy, which would have no effect on the surrounding tissue.

Medical and Biological Research

If a laser beam can be made narrow enough, it can be used to perform microsurgery on the energy-converting portions of the nuclei of cells and on portions of the chromosomes. This is likely to open up a whole range of fascinating experiments that might well lead to practical means of diagnosing and treating malfunctions of the human body. To make the laser beams narrow they have been sent down microscopes, and such beams have brought about changes in the characteristics of individual cells, causing them to increase or slow down their action. Changes have been produced in both red and white blood cells. A team led by Dr. Marcel Bessis of Paris has treated areas of tissue only 10,000-25,000 A. in diameter, and some photographs taken by them appear on page 132.

The laser may make it possible to measure, for the first time, the resolving power of the retina of the human eye. Resolving power is a measure of the ability to distinguish objects that are very close to each other. The resolving power of the complete eye can easily be measured by looking at a grating made up of very fine parallel lines displayed on a screen, and bringing the lines closer and closer to each other until they appear to merge. The closer the lines are when this happens, the higher is the resolving power of the eye. Such a measurement, however, gives the combined resolving power of the optical system (the cornea, the humors, and the lens) and the retina. It does not tell us the resolving power of the retina alone.

One way to measure the resolving power of the retina alone would be to produce interference fringes on the retina. The experiment is illustrated on page 134. Coherent light of the kind

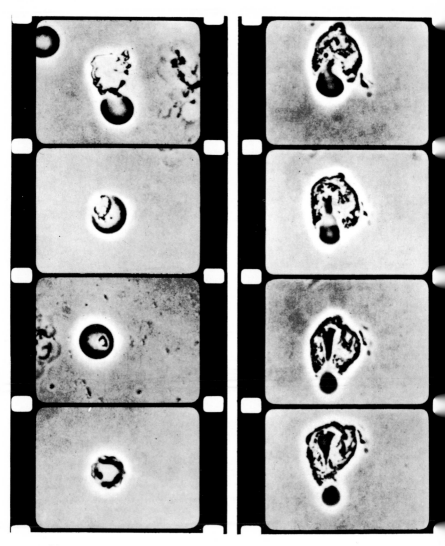

Above: the sequence of photographs in the left-hand column shows a red blood cell (the dark, well-defined object) being sectioned by an attacking phagocyte. The right-hand column shows comparable laser-produced effects—lesions produced in red blood cells by a laser beam. The beam intensity decreases from top to bottom. The apparatus used to take these photographs is shown opposite.

Opposite, top: a laser being used to treat skin cancer on a patient's legs.

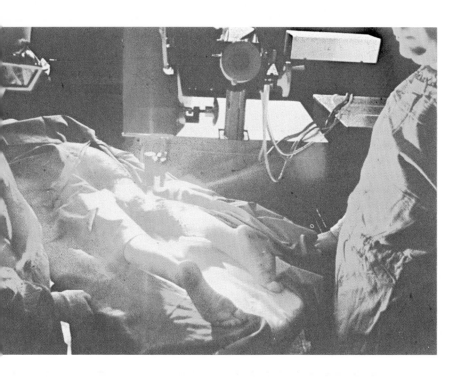

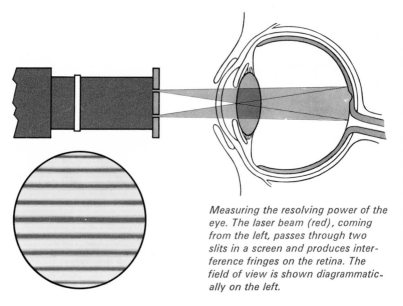

Measuring the resolving power of the eye. The laser beam (red), coming from the left, passes through two slits in a screen and produces interference fringes on the retina. The field of view is shown diagrammatically on the left.

produced by a laser shines onto a screen containing two very fine parallel slits, much as in Young's experiments (see page 31). The light passes through the slits but is blocked everywhere else. The screen is close to the eye, and light waves from the slits interfere and produce fringes on the retina. The spacing of these fringes depends on the wavelength and on how far apart the slits are, but not on the optical system of the eye.

In the experiment, the spacing of the fringes would be altered by changing either the separation of the slits or the wavelength of the light. Eventually, they would appear to merge, and the point at which this happens tells us the resolving power. This experiment could, in principle, be done with any source of coherent light, but a laser would be the most convenient type.

Dr. I. Chisholm, of the University of Glasgow, has suggested that laser light may help to solve a long-standing ornithological riddle. His idea concerns the *pecten*—a peculiar, dark, trapezium-shaped structure protruding from the retina of a bird into the space inside its eyeball (see the photograph opposite). This structure had already caught the attention of workers in the 17th century, but its function is still unknown. One suggestion is that the pecten is a nutritive organ concerned partly with the maintenance of the retina and partly with the control of fluid exchange in the eye. This idea is supported by the fact that the bird's eye has no blood vessels leading to different parts of the retina, while the pecten contains a dense network of blood vessels. However, these vessels, including even the smallest capillaries, have a thick glossy coat that makes the diffusion of nutrients through them highly unlikely, if not impossible. A second theory is that it serves as a heating organ to keep the retina from cooling down.

One way of deciding between the rival theories would be to cut the pecten out surgically and see what effect this had; but even slight interference with the eyeball during the operation would invalidate the results of such an experiment. Dr. Chisholm and his colleagues believe that a laser beam may be able to destroy the pecten without damaging other parts of the eye. They propose to destroy the pecten in one eye of a domestic hen, a bird with a well-developed pecten. If the eye becomes blind, the pecten must have a nutritive function. If there is no impairment, the pecten must be merely a vestigial relic in hens.

An opened-up section of a bird's eye showing the pecten (the dark area at bottom left).

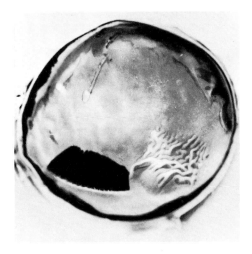

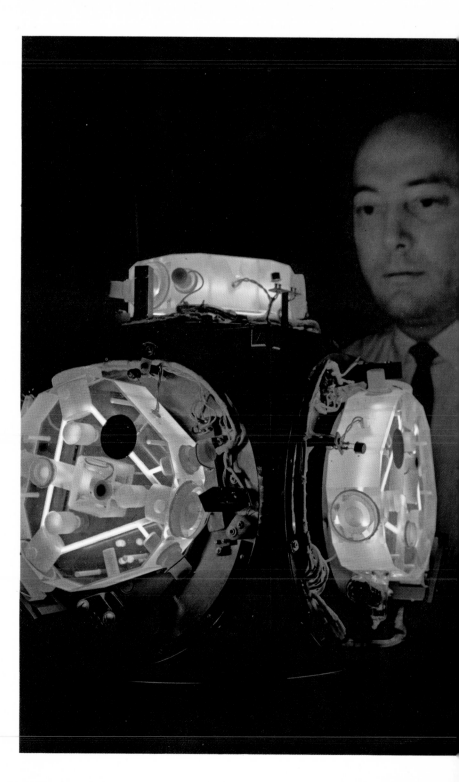

6 Location and Measurement

Locating objects accurately and measuring their distances from fixed points has been one of the most important fields of application of the laser. This field is probably attracting more money from the armed services—that prime supplier of funds for research and development—than any other connected with lasers. But for this military interest, the laser would probably still be no more than an interesting scientific development without practical applications.

There was military interest in, and financial backing for, lasers even before the first one was demonstrated. In those days the armed services hoped that the laser would turn out to be that long-sought-after military weapon, the death-ray. Unfortunately, or perhaps fortunately, the power levels available from present-day lasers and the levels likely to be available from future optical lasers seem to rule out this idea. Hans Thirring, professor of theoretical physics at the University of Vienna, showed that there were theoretical flaws in the concept of a laser death-ray in an

A three-axis gyroscope. Each of the three units is a ring laser drilled in solid fused quartz and containing two laser beams, one moving around clockwise, the other anticlockwise. If the laser rotates about its axis, the frequencies of the two beams become unequal and the difference can be used to measure the rate of rotation.

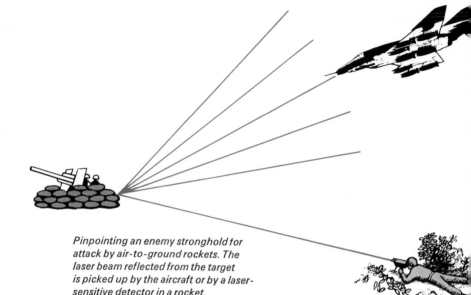

Pinpointing an enemy stronghold for attack by air-to-ground rockets. The laser beam reflected from the target is picked up by the aircraft or by a laser-sensitive detector in a rocket.

article in the British weekly journal *New Scientist* in 1963.

However, the development of the carbon dioxide laser, which is considerably more powerful and efficient than earlier types (see page 42), has reawakened interest in the idea of using lasers as weapons. It still seems very unlikely that we shall ever develop a true death-ray—that is, a ray capable of killing or injuring large numbers of soldiers, or of damaging military vehicles or aircraft. But the beam from a carbon dioxide laser is quite capable of setting fire to the clothing of an infantryman from far off. In other words, though not an *efficient* means of killing people, the laser might be useful as a psychological weapon. The effect on the morale of troops of having their clothes set on fire by a silent, invisible beam can easily be imagined.

There is also considerable interest in the laser as a means of pinpointing enemy troops and installations in the congested battle conditions found in guerrilla wars. Locating such targets for the benefit of attacking aircraft, for instance, is particularly difficult in jungle conditions. The United States Army hope that lasers can be used to ensure that both artillery and high-speed aircraft can pick out targets selected by ground troops without the risk of hitting their own men. In one proposed scheme, the ground troops would aim a laser beam at the target, which would scatter the light in all directions. A laser detector and television screen in an attacking aircraft could pick up the energy and accurately locate the point from which it was being scattered. The pilot could then make his attack with guns or rockets, or he could fire an air-to-ground guided missile sensitive to the laser energy. The target-seeking head in the missile would lock on to the target and home on to it. In tests carried out by the General Dynamics Company in the United States, a 120-cm-square target illuminated by the beam from a cooled gallium arsenide laser has been successfully destroyed by a ground-launched supersonic missile guided in this way.

It has been suggested that lasers could be used to destroy intercontinental ballistic missiles and this idea caused considerable interest in the early 1960s. But Professor Thirring pointed out that more than 800 kW would be needed for about a minute to destroy the nuclear warhead of such a missile at a height of 50 km. Only a small fraction of the original laser beam would actually strike the warhead, and when allowances were made for this it turned out that the laser would have to generate some 160 MW continuously for that minute—far in excess of anything likely to be available. It is even doubtful whether the amount of energy required could be transmitted through the atmosphere at all because such a beam would ionize molecules in the air. On the other hand, it might only be necessary to damage the warhead slightly to ensure its eventual destruction. Even a very small scratch in the protective coating of the warhead would cause it to burn up as it reentered the atmosphere. A ballistic missile defense system based on the laser seems very remote, but not hopeless, and the services are still spending considerable sums of money on projects of this sort.

Laser Range Finders
The first laser military equipment likely to be operational is the battlefield range finder, which enables infantrymen and tank gunners to measure the range of a target several miles away with an accuracy of a few meters. The laser range finder scores over existing microwave radio range finders by virtue of its much narrower beam width. Microwave radio range finders suffer from the

A laser range finder in use. The instrument contains three telescopes: the first for aiming the instrument by eye, the second for transmitting light, and the third for picking up the reflected light.

errors introduced when targets lie roughly in the same direction, but at different distances. It is often impossible, for example, to determine the distance of an enemy tank because of echoes from trees and houses that, although not directly in line with the tank, are close enough to lie within the fairly wide radio beam. Laser beams, on the other hand, are for practical purposes nondivergent over the relatively short distances encountered on the battlefield.

Up to now there has been some difficulty with laser range finders because the ruby lasers employed in them are sensitive to changes of temperature. In particular, spurious measurements can result from *double pulsing*—when the ruby produces two pulses of light when it should only produce one—an effect that occurs in very cold weather. The receiving equipment finds it difficult to distinguish between the two pulses.

In spite of problems like this, a laser range finder will be incorporated in the fire control system of the MBT–70 tank, a joint development of the United States and West German armies that is destined to be the main battle tank of the 1970s. Light, portable range finders weighing as little as 9 kg. have been developed that can be carried by forward artillery observers as well as in tanks.

There are also many civil applications for laser range finders. They are used for ground surveys and are likely to be very important in the field of geodetic surveying. It seems likely that the positions of continents and islands can be fixed to within a few meters with laser range finders, which compares well with the accuracy of several hundred meters achieved so far using conventional methods.

There are three ways in which a laser can be used for measuring distances, all based on a comparison of the radiation scattered from a target with the original radiation from the laser. The comparison is usually made at the same site as the laser transmitter; but it can be made at the target location, or even at an entirely independent location if this is more convenient or more accurate. The technique easiest to understand is that of measuring the time taken for a laser pulse to travel from the laser to the target and back again. This is the technique developed during the 1930s for use at radio frequencies, which led to the development of radar. Light travels at an enormous speed (3×10^{10} cm. per second) but electronic circuits can easily measure the time intervals involved with great accuracy even though they may be only a few millionths of a second long.

Alternatively, the light returning from the target can be mixed with light leaving the laser to produce an interference pattern. This technique is capable of very great accuracy, because the basic dimension of the pattern is the wavelength of light. The third technique consists of modulating the laser beam by varying its amplitude at a microwave radio frequency. The timing of the modulation of the echo can be compared with the modulation of the transmitted laser beam. The comparison tells us whether the distance traveled by the beam is equal to a whole number of modulation patterns and, if not, by what fraction of the pattern length they differ. The method does not, by itself, tell us the overall distance but it can be used to measure small changes in distance very accurately. It was used in Japan, for example, during the building of a dam, to measure the movement of the top of the dam as the water flowed in.

High power is essential when using the pulse method, because the laser is switched on for only very short intervals in each second. This is why ruby lasers are usually employed. They have very large power outputs when producing single pulses or a series of pulses at a fairly low repetition rate. The giant-pulse technique described in Chapter 2 is commonly used to switch the ruby lasers on and off. The Q-switch may be of the type described there, using a rotating prism or the electrooptical effect in a Kerr cell. Another popular type consists of a simple cell of a liquid in which there is a solution of bleachable dye such as phthalocyanine or cryptocyanine. These normally absorb light in the red part of the spectrum very heavily but suddenly become transparent when illuminated with light of really high intensity.

- The accuracy with which distances can be measured by the pulse technique depends upon the accuracy with which the elapsed time can be measured and the accuracy with which the velocity of light is known. With modern electronic circuits, elapsed time can be measured to an accuracy of about one nanosecond $(= 10^{-9}$ seconds), which corresponds to a distance of 30 cm., or 15 out and 15 back. The speed of light is known to about one part in 100,000, so the overall accuracy can be expected to vary from about one part in 1000 for short ranges to about one part in 100,000 over the very long distances—100 miles or more—encountered when measuring distances to clouds, layers of air turbulence, the moon, satellites, and other targets of that kind.

Light beams have been used in distance-measuring equipment for surveying and geodetic work for some years, but they are obtained from incoherent sources and for large distances the method suffers from the wide spread of the beam and the poor selectivity of receivers designed to work with incoherent light. Microwave radio beams are also used extensively in the surveying field, but they suffer from the same disadvantages as battlefield distance-measuring equipment (see pages 139-140).

Probably the best way of designing a laser instrument for high-precision surveying would be to use the microwave modulation technique. The nature of laser light makes it possible to use modulating frequencies as high as 10 million megacycles per second, and modern electronic circuits will allow accurate measurement to be made of the time it takes for a given modulation envelope to return to the receiver.

Lasers in Geodesy

Rather paradoxically, one of the first results of the space age has been a much more accurate knowledge of the shape of our own planet. Artificial satellites of the earth make it possible to measure distances of many thousands of kilometers on the earth's surface at a single step, and several countries are establishing a unified global network of surveying points that will enable the positions of the continents and islands to be fixed with an accuracy many times greater than before.

Surveyors use satellites in much the same way as they use hills and accurately known survey points on earth, in the technique known as *triangulation*. This technique has been in use for many centuries and can be applied to satellites just as easily as to terrestrial survey points. Triangles are formed between two known points and an unknown point, and the position of the unknown point can be calculated from the distance between the known points and the angles of the triangle. Satellite triangulation scores over classical terrestrial methods in that the triangles can have much longer sides. Hundreds of kilometers can be measured with classical methods, but distances of many thousands of kilometers can be measured directly using satellite triangulation techniques. These long distances can, of course, be measured by terrestrial methods—over land, at least—by adding up the results of measurements made over a succession of shorter distances, but the errors in each measurement accumulate to make this process rather inaccurate.

Early surveys by satellite used microwave radio distance-measuring equipment mounted on the ground or on the satellite, but there seems little doubt that laser-based optical methods will find increasing use in the future. Radio systems suffer from the refraction that occurs in the atmosphere and especially in the ionosphere. The latter is a belt of ionized gas in the upper regions

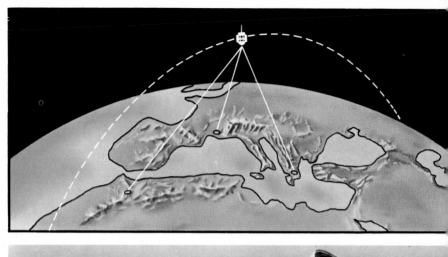

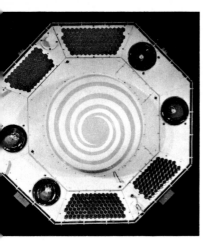

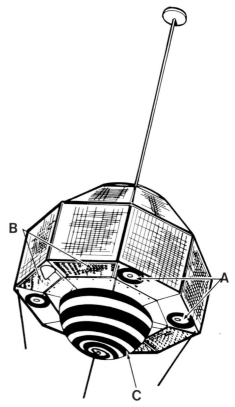

Diagram (right) and photograph (above) of a Geos-A satellite intended for geodetic measurements, showing flashing lights (A), laser reflectors (B), and spiral antenna (C). The flashing lights, which are conventional, non-laser lights, are for preliminary sighting and can be switched on from the ground.

Opposite, top: triangulation by satellite. The distances and bearings of a geodetic satellite from three points on the earth's surface are measured. The photograph below shows a camera used for tracking satellites at the Royal Radar Establishment, England. Sunlight reflected from the satellite produces a track on the photographic plate. A similar technique could be used with light reflected from a ground-based laser.

of the atmosphere. Light waves are not affected by the ionosphere, and other errors can be avoided by making the measurements relative to the background stars whose light suffers the same amount of refraction. A fairly simple satellite, such as the Echo balloon type, can be used and the observing system can be cheap and compact. Of course measurements can be made only when the sky is clear at two or more observing stations, which may be thousands of kilometers apart.

Optical systems have advantages over radio systems then, but

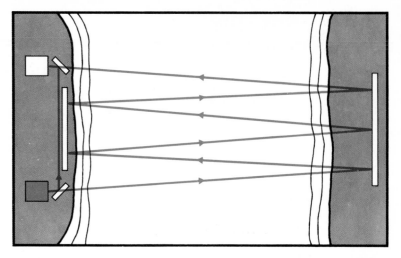

Are the continents drifting apart ? A laser might be used to measure such drift.
The beam would be reflected to-and-fro several thousand times, not just three,
as in the diagram. Continental drift would cause a change in frequency that
would show up when the beam was compared with another from the same laser.

this still does not mean that lasers have to be used. Many surveys have been carried out in which Echo balloon satellites reflected sunlight to observing stations on the ground. The snag here is that measurements have to be made when the observers are in darkness while the satellite is in sunlight, which rather restricts the measurement times.

Satellites used with lasers can be either *passive* or *active*. The former simply reflect light from a ground-based laser, and the Echo balloon type, which is used with sunlight, could equally well be used with laser light. Active satellites would actually carry a laser and send its light to the ground.

Quite massive cameras must be used to record the light from a satellite. These are usually of the fixed direction type, such as the one at the Royal Radar Establishment in England shown in the photograph on page 144. These cameras are adjusted to point at the part of the sky through which the satellite is expected to pass at the observation time. Two accurately timed shutters are fitted. One operates several times a second to provide breaks in the satellite trail on the photographic plate for measurement purposes. The other shutter operates at a much slower rate and provides breaks in the trails of the stars. These breaks on the developed plates provide accurate time markers, and the star images enable the direction in which the camera is pointed at specific moments of time to be determined precisely. Measurements of the distance to a satellite at a height of 1500 km. can be made with an accuracy of 2 or 3 m., and higher accuracies should be possible when lasers with greater power and shorter pulse length are available. Up to early 1967, the most successful work of this kind had been done by the United States National Aeronautics and Space Administration at the Goddard Center and the Smithsonian Institution. However the French will probably achieve greater accuracies with their Diademe satellites, which are intended to orbit at a maximum altitude of 1000 km. The French have laser tracking stations at St. Michel de Provence in the South of France, at Corinth in Greece, and at Colomb-Bechar in Algeria. A complete surveying experiment involves observing a satellite from all three stations simultaneously. Two of these measurements fix the position of the satellite in relation to the ground, and the third determines the relationship of the landmass of Africa to that of Europe.

Continental Drift

It seems likely that the great accuracies obtainable with laser measuring techniques will shed light on many problems, including the much-debated question of continental drift. There is a theory that the continents are moving relative to one another because of internal convection currents that emerge at the surface of the earth along structural lines such as the mid-Atlantic Ridge. Recent conjectures on this subject have postulated an average drift velocity of 2 to 4 cm. a year. Accurate measurements of drift velocities of this order might be possible using an earth-based technique suggested by W. Hornig, of Hornig Laboratories, New York. There are certain areas, such as the Strait of Gibraltar and the Strait of Aden, where large and distinct landmasses lie in relative proximity on either side of a structural line. Hornig's idea is to place a laser on one continental landmass and a detector on the other and to try to detect the *Doppler shift* in the frequency of the laser beam. The Doppler shift is the apparent change in frequency that occurs when a source of waves is moving toward or away from an observer. The best-known example is the sudden

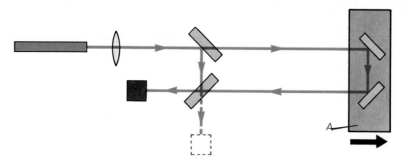

The distance moved in the laboratory by the carriage (A) can be measured very accurately by combining the laser light reflected from the carriage with direct light from the same source to produce an interference pattern. With only one detector, the direction of the movement (backward or forward) cannot be distinguished. Adding a second detector (dashed lines) overcomes this problem.

change in the pitch of a locomotive whistle as the train rushes past. When the train is moving toward someone, his ears receive more waves per second than the whistle is actually giving out—in other words, he hears a note higher than the whistle's true pitch. When the train is moving away, on the other hand, the listener hears a lower note than the true pitch. The same effect occurs with electromagnetic waves, and if one of the two landmasses is moving relative to the other, the light received at the detector will have a frequency slightly different from its original frequency. In the case of the train and its whistle the change of frequency is easily noticeable. But the velocity of light is huge compared to that of sound, and the velocity of drift—if any—is minute in comparison, with the result that any Doppler shift would be tiny. In fact, it would be far too small to be measured if the experiment were carried out in the simple way described so far. The shift could be increased, however, if both laser and detector were on the same landmass, as shown in the diagram on page 146, and the laser beam were reflected to and fro many times. Finally, it would be mixed with part of the laser output obtained directly and the Doppler shift frequency extracted as the difference between the direct and reflected beams. Calculations show that if the reflecting surfaces were 10 miles apart the beam could be induced to make approximately 500 round trips, giving a shift of about two cycles per second.

The difficulty with this experiment is that variations in atmospheric temperature and pressure would cause changes in the optical path length between the mirrors, which would mask the change due to continental drift. But these variations would produce random fluctuations in path length, whereas the drift would produce a steady effect, and there is some hope that this difference would allow that part of the change that is due to drift to be detected against the background noise. What is needed is a filter that would respond to a particular frequency and reject all others.

Since we have some idea what the continental drift velocity ought to be, we can estimate the frequency of the returning light. The filter would be tuned in turn to frequencies at and about this estimated one, and there should be a maximum in the average intensity of the transmitted light at exactly the frequency resulting from continental drift. Conventional electronic filters would not be sensitive enough, but the laser-based optical filters described in the next chapter might be able to do the job.

Counting Fringes

Techniques in which the light reflected from a moving object is mixed with, and interferes with, light coming directly from the same original source have been used for many years to measure distances very accurately. The two beams of light produce light and dark fringes that indicate their relative phases. As the object moves, the fringes cross the field of view, and the total number of fringes moving past a fixed line enables us to calculate how far the object has moved. The American scientist A. A. Michelson used a technique like this when he measured an intermediate standard during his classic determination of the meter in terms of the wavelength of light. He counted up to 1000 fringes by eye. Today, electronic counting methods can be used, which are much more convenient; but with conventional sources the counting rate is limited to perhaps 10 or 100 fringes per second because of the very low intensity of the light.

The far higher intensity of the laser beam overcomes this problem and counting rates of at least a million per second, which correspond to movements as fast as 30 cm. per second, can now be achieved. If we can measure the rate at which the fringes move we can calculate how fast the reflecting object is moving. The exceptionally narrow bandwidth of the laser is another advantage, because it makes it possible to detect interference even when the object is many thousands of kilometers away. This is in complete contrast to conventional sources, for which the limit is only 30 or 40 cm.

Scientists at the National Physical Laboratory at Teddington, England, have developed a machine of this type for measuring length scales of various kinds. It will measure distances up to one meter and has a discrimination of about one four-millionth of a centimeter. The red light from a helium-neon laser is used. It falls onto a semitransparent mirror, and part of it is reflected onto a second semitransparent mirror as in the diagram on page 148. From there, the light is reflected onto a detector (a photoelectric cell). A portion of the original light passes straight through the first mirror and falls onto the moving carriage, and it is the distance moved by this carriage that is to be measured. A mirror system on the carriage reflects the light back through the second semitransparent mirror and onto the photoelectric cell. Thus, direct light from the laser and reflected light from the carriage fall onto the detector and interfere with each other. For one position of the carriage the two beams will be in phase at the detector and will thus interfere constructively, giving a high output from the detector. If the carriage moves a quarter wavelength away from the mirrors, the extra distance traveled by the reflected beam will be half a wavelength. The two beams will then be out of phase at the detector and will interfere destructively. Under these conditions, there will be no output from the detector. Thus any movement of the carriage toward or away from the detector will cause the output from it to alternate between a high value and zero. Zero points will occur for each quarter wavelength movement of the carriage. The carriage is made to move between the two points whose distance apart is required, and the result tells us the distance in terms of the wavelength of light.

In the basic arrangement, using only one detector, the direction of movement of the carriage cannot be resolved. This is something of a disadvantage in a practical instrument because vibrations of the carriage, either while it is stationary or while it is moving, will give spurious readings. This effect can be avoided by having a second detector in the position shown by the box marked by dashes in the diagram. This detector receives direct light that has passed straight through the second semitransparent mirror. Some of the light reflected from the carriage is reflected again at the second mirror and also falls on the second detector. The difference between the outputs of the two detectors can be used to determine the direction of movement of the carriage, and spurious readings eliminated in this way.

Counting fringes can be an extremely accurate way of measuring small changes in distance and is likely to have many new applications now that lasers are available. Earthquake-sensing devices of various kinds have been developed at the Hornig Laboratories. Their original purpose was to supplement existing instruments in the study of distant earthquakes, but it has recently been suggested that laser instruments could be used to give early warning of a major earthquake. It seems clear that major landslips are preceded by several days of minor slips of a sort that could be detected by a laser instrument. A research project is currently under way in California to see whether this system will work. A battery of laser instruments spread over a large area will measure earth tremors and feed the information to a central computing center. It is hoped that clear patterns indicating the likelihood of a major earthquake will be detected in time to give 24 or 48 hours' notice to the local population.

Laser Gyroscopes

Lasers can be used to measure angles as well as distances. The Honeywell Corporation of the United States delivered a laser gyroscope drilled from a solid block of quartz to the United States Naval Ordnance Test Section at China Lake in the latter part of 1966. The great attraction of laser gyroscopes is their ability to sense extremely high rotation rates. A conventional gyroscope mounted in a vehicle that makes a sudden turn will take several minutes to settle down on the new bearing. Laser gyroscopes contain no mechanical motors of the type found in conventional gyroscopes and respond instantly to a sudden turn. They also contain none of the magnetic and temperature-

152

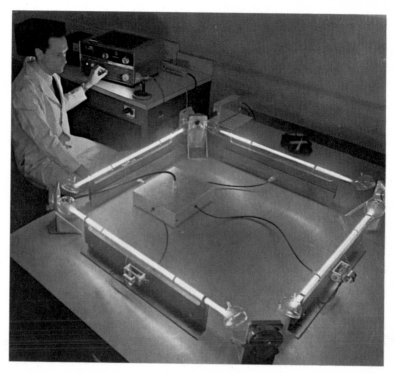

Above: a ring laser, containing two beams traveling around the square in opposite directions. This experiment led to the first attempt at building a laser gyroscope (opposite page, top left), which used conventional glass tubes for laser cavities, but was in the form of a triangle rather than a square.

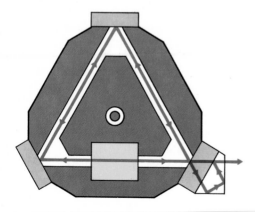

Left and opposite: the latest version of the laser gyroscope is made from a solid block of quartz with paths for the light beams drilled in it. The diagram shows the laser itself (yellow) and, at bottom right, the combiner prism for bringing the two beams together so they can be compared.

Opposite, top right: the next stage in developing laser gyroscopes was to study the concept of a three-axis gyroscope, as shown by the model.

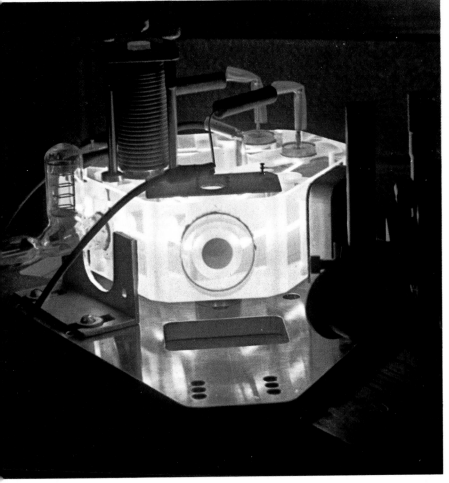

sensitive elements found in conventional gyroscopes, and can be started instantly. A conventional gyroscope can take from 15 to 30 minutes to reach its working speed and a steady temperature, and this can be a serious disadvantage, particularly in military systems. The laser gyroscope is also much more rugged than the conventional type, and its operation is not affected by the high accelerations encountered during takeoff and maneuver of spacecraft and missiles. A laser gyroscope will continue to operate and feed information into control systems even when a rocket is going through periods of peak acceleration.

The first person to describe how a laser beam could be used in a gyroscope was A. H. Rosenthal, of the Kollsman Instrument Corporation, in a paper presented to the Optical Society of America in August 1961. The basic idea is to make a laser in the form of a ring, as shown in the photograph on page 152. The mirrors at *both* ends are semitransparent so that two laser beams are generated within a closed optical loop. One beam travels around the loop clockwise and the other anticlockwise. If the ship or aircraft is maintaining a steady course, the closed loop is stationary and the two beams take the same time to traverse it; but if the ship or aircraft changes course, the loop will rotate about its axis. When this happens the effective path for one beam is shortened, while the path for the other beam is made longer. This introduces relativistic effects that alter the frequencies of the two beams in opposite directions.

This difference of frequency can be detected and interpreted without difficulty by electronic circuits. All that is needed is some way of extracting the two beams and allowing them to interfere and produce a series of fringes, and this can be done with a combiner prism, as shown in the diagram on page 152. The fringe pattern will move when the ship or aircraft changes direction, and the number of fringes crossing a suitably placed detector each second will be proportional to the rate of rotation. Each fringe thus represents precisely an angle through which the ship or aircraft has turned.

Early laser gyroscopes, such as the one in the top left-hand photograph on page 153, suffered from the fragile nature of the mirrors and laser tubes used. They very quickly became maladjusted and a separate, bulky frame was needed to provide a firm mounting. The success of the later models, such as the one produced by Honeywell (see the large photograph on the same page), is based on the use of the solid block of high quality fused quartz mentioned earlier. The beam paths are produced by machining and drilling holes and cavities into the block, and the mirrors are mounted at the corners of the block by molecular adhesion. The mirrors and the block thus form a rugged unit. The interior of the quartz block is evacuated and filled with a mixture of helium and neon gases. Using a quartz block greatly simplifies the manufacturing process, and it seems likely that laser gyroscopes will be only about one fifth of the price of conventional gyroscopes.

Laser Radar

Laser radar is a somewhat more sophisticated version of the distance-measuring equipment described earlier in this chapter. It works in much the same way as conventional microwave radar, the only major difference being that the microwave transmitter and receiver are replaced by a laser and an optical receiver. The narrow beam width of the laser and its high frequency mean that it can be used in a short-range radar system of much higher definition than is possible with microwaves.

At the moment, for example, it is possible to navigate a ship along a coastline and into a relatively narrow river such as the Mersey, the Thames, or even the Rhine; but the definition of conventional radar is not high enough to allow the ship to enter a complicated dock system such as that at Liverpool. The relatively large wavelength of microwaves means that the beam is quite wide and it is impossible to see the walls of the lock gates and quays with sufficient accuracy. Here a laser radar would score heavily. Its greater sensitivity to fog and mist would not be important because the laser beam would be able to traverse the relatively short distances involved in even the thickest of fogs.

Laser radar would also prove invaluable in space, where its high-definition qualities can be used at long range as well as short because of the lack of atmospheric attenuation. It has been used for experimental purposes on earth, within the atmosphere.

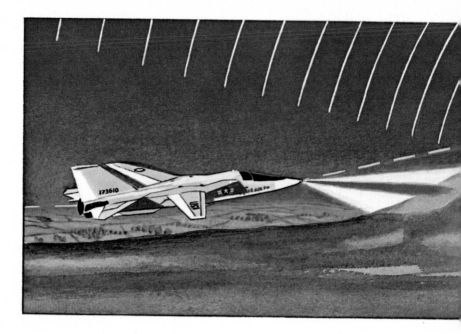

To avoid detection, an attacking aircraft flies close to the ground (path shown by yellow line). It is piloted automatically, with radar (white) feeding back information about the terrain ahead. A laser beam (red) would give much better discrimination and accuracy, and allow the aircraft to fly closer to the ground.

In England, for example, an electricity generating board has been using a laser radar to plot the path of otherwise invisible smoke plumes from the chimneys of oil-, coal- and gas-fired electricity generating stations. A proposed use for a fairly sophisticated laser radar system is shown in the diagram above.

Lasers under Water

There was great interest during the early part of the 1960s in the possibility of using laser beams to detect deep-diving submarines, using a sort of underwater laser radar. This interest was sparked off by the inadequacies of the existing sound-based detection systems (sonar), which cannot detect submarines at very great depths. Unfortunately it turned out that laser beams, too, were heavily attenuated in seawater; but the United States navy, among others, has not given up the idea of an underwater laser radar. There is still hope that some specific wavelength will be found that can penetrate the otherwise opaque seawater for

great distances. Like many other topics in underwater technology, the search for a suitable wavelength is hampered by lack of knowledge of the oceans and their characteristics. However, great sums of money are being spent on the subject at the moment. During 1967 the United States navy started testing a portable blue-green laser developed by the Avco Corporation, which they hope can be combined with existing sonar for such tasks as guiding torpedoes and distinguishing between real enemy submarines and decoys. They are also using a neodymium yttrium aluminum garnet laser developed by the Korad Corporation to study the absorption and scattering properties of water. By means of frequency doubling in a nonlinear crystal (see Chapter 7) the infrared output of this laser is converted into a green beam on 5300 A., which is one of the best wavelengths found so far for penetrating seawater.

7 Cutting and Calculating

Goldfinger's attempt to kill James Bond with a laser in his Swiss laboratory was probably the first occasion on which the general public saw a laser in use. The producers of the film had obviously used poetic licence; but the attempt did illustrate one of the most dramatic applications of the laser—cutting and machining—and there is little doubt that an organization as large and efficient as Goldfinger's would have had a laser cutting machine, at least as a research tool, at that time.

Just what are the real advantages of the laser over more conventional cutting tools, and where is it most likely to be used in this respect in the future? Its three chief advantages are its directionality, its high peak power, and the fact that its energy is in a radiant form. These advantages are very real indeed, but it is worth while realizing from the outset that the average power output from most lasers is no higher than that of a soldering iron and their efficiency is very low. It is the extent to which the power is concentrated that is remarkable. It seems likely, there-

The general public's first glimpse of a "laser" was probably this scene from the film Goldfinger, in which Goldfinger threatens James Bond with a lethal-looking but unrealistically large solid-state model.

A focused laser beam causes electrical breakdown of air by ionizing the molecules.

fore, that the laser cutting tool will be used where the actual amount of work to be done is limited, but where the work is of a particularly precise nature.

The laser would be very useful where the cutting energy has to be supplied to a target much smaller than the source of the energy. Conventional sources tend to radiate their energy in all directions and most of their output is wasted in an application like this. With a laser, on the other hand, it would not be very hard to focus the entire energy of the beam onto an extremely small target. Much the same sort of argument applies in the case where the target has to be rather a long way away. Such a target would subtend only a small angle at the source and here again almost all the energy from a conventional source would be wasted. Roughly speaking, the directionality of the laser will give it the advantage, in short-range work, if the target is measured in millimeters or fractions of a millimeter, but for larger targets there is little difficulty in focusing the energy from a conventional source such as a plasma torch, which would probably be more efficient and powerful, and possibly cheaper as well.

For these reasons it seemed likely until a few years ago that the main scope for laser cutting tools would be in drilling very small holes in special materials and components. Exotic applications seemed to be the only likely ones. But a firm of men's tailors has recently announced plans to cut out many thousands of suits with a laser beam controlled by a computer. This somewhat unexpected application illustrates another advantage of the laser cutting tool: the ease with which the beam can be directed onto moving targets, either manually or—more significantly—under automatic control.

In a sense it is inaccurate to speak of lasers as "cutting tools," because they achieve their effect by heat rather than by physical force. With giant-pulse lasers the temperatures produced in the target can be well over 100,000°C. Such high temperatures are generally an advantage, of course, but beams as powerful as this can create difficulties. Focusing such a beam may result in electrical breakdown of the air it passes through, as in the photograph opposite. This prevents the beam from converging properly and the ionized air is so strongly absorbing that it can trap most of the laser energy and prevent it reaching the target. T. P. Hughes of the National Physical Laboratory has suggested that the most efficient way of drilling a hole might be first of all to melt the material that is to be removed, using a comparatively weak laser pulse, and then to direct a short, very-high-power pulse at the molten metal to vaporize a thin layer on the front surface. The atoms thrown out from the surface as it vaporized would exert a tremendous kick—more scientifically, a tremendous kinetic pressure—that would expel a complete cylindrical plug of molten metal. That such an evaporation kick occurs is obvious from the loud click heard when a giant pulse is fired at a metal surface, and by the buckled appearance at the back of a plate after it has been subjected to such pulses.

Drilling, Cutting, Etching, and Welding

One of the earliest demonstrations of laser-beam drilling was when the General Electric Company succeeded in boring through diamond, the hardest substance known to man. A laser drill is now being used on the production line by another company, Western Electric, to pierce holes in the diamonds used in making wire-drawing dies (used for making wire by drawing

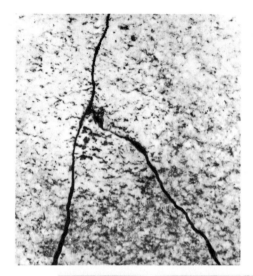

Left: the effect of an unfocused laser beam shining for 30 seconds on a piece of granite.

Below: apparatus used at the Massachusetts Institute of Technology for studying the effects of laser radiation on materials. The photograph on the left was taken during these experiments.

Opposite page: a laser beam burns a hole in diamond, the hardest material known to man.

metal through them). It takes about two minutes to pierce
each diamond, compared with the two or three days it takes to
grind out a hole in the conventional way with diamond dust.
The hole must still be honed with diamond dust to bring it to
the exact size, because the laser-made hole is a little rough, but
even so the total time is much less than with conventional
techniques. The laser used has a power output of 10 joules and
fires a pulse a second. The operator protects himself from the
beam by using closed-circuit television, which also gives him
60-fold magnification, to observe the process. It may one day be
possible to do without the final honing process by arranging
for the laser beam to pass through a converging lens system
that will concentrate the main beam and reject any peripheral
light that might cause irregularities in the hole.

Another proposed application is correcting the balance of a
component, such as an armature, that is under test on a dynamic

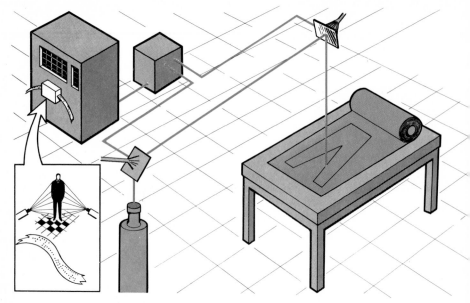

Automated tailoring. Stereoscopic cameras photograph the client, and the information is converted into a punched-tape record of his contours (inset). At the factory, the tape is fed into a computer controlling a system of mirrors that guide the laser beam (shown in red).

balancing machine. Even a small imbalance in an armature will cause serious vibrations in the electric motor of which it will eventually form a part. A laser pulse aimed at it could remove small fractions of a gram from appropriate places, and if this operation were linked to the rotation of the balancing machine, extremely fast correction could be achieved.

Cutting suits is not, perhaps, an activity in which one would expect revolutionary techniques to be employed, but the very large tailoring group with a chain of stores is in fact a complex manufacturing and selling organization. The British company Montague Burton makes one and a quarter million made-to-measure suits a year, each of which takes a skilled tailor 30 minutes to cut out. Automation of some sort could obviously bring great benefits in a production process of this magnitude, but the Company's research department found it impossible to imagine a pair of scissors controlled by a computer. Hot knives, hot wires, flame jets, and sparks have all been tried. Of these, only the sparks worked at all well, but even with this method the result was a series of holes rather than a clean, continuous cut. A laser beam is capable of cutting through a double thickness of synthetic cloth and leaving neatly melted edges behind it. A cutting rate as fast as 3 m. a minute can be achieved with the carbon dioxide laser supplied to Burton's by Elliott Brothers Limited. This Company hopes to be able to deliver a much more powerful laser in a few years' time that will do the job perhaps 20 times as fast, allowing suits to be cut out in a couple of minutes.

This is a good example of a process where the special qualities of the laser are of great benefit and where its choice is almost inevitable. Burton's hopes eventually to develop a fully automated system that will work as shown in the diagram opposite. The process will start off with the customer being photographed by a special stereoscopic camera that will map the contours of his body exactly. The photographs will then be analyzed electronically and details of the customer's shape printed out on punched tape in a form suitable for feeding into a computer. At the factory, the computer will assemble batches of orders and issue instructions to the laser cloth-cutter. The laser and cutting table will probably be fixed, and the beam will be guided along the proper path by a system of moving mirrors controlled by the computer.

Another application of computer-controlled laser pulses may be etching the halftone plates used for printing, which could be done in a few seconds—far quicker than by conventional methods. Halftone printing plates apply ink to paper from a surface that stands out physically above the background. In the past, chemical methods have been used to eat away the background after the points that have to stand out have been coated with an acid-resisting material. More recently, electronically controlled tools have been used to gouge out the background areas from metal or plastic plates, the tools being driven by signals from a photoelectric cell scanning the picture to be printed.

A laser etching tool would make use of the fact that when a pulsed laser beam is focused to a point on a metal surface a fragment of the metal is vaporized, leaving behind a small cone-shaped crater. Repeated pulses from the laser beam would burn a

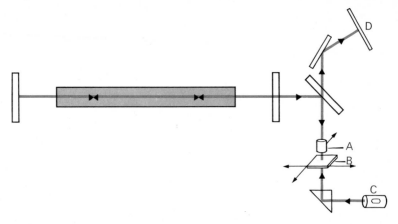

Laser micromachining. The beam from a helium-neon laser is focused by the lens (A) onto the glass substrate (B). The lamp (C) provides conventional light that projects an image of the substrate pattern onto the screen (D) for the operator to view. The substrate can move in the horizontal plane, its movement being controlled by a computer. There is a layer of silicon just below the glass. Silicon is vaporized by the beam and strikes the underside of the substrate where it is deposited on the cool glass. The technique, shown also in the photograph opposite, is used to make photolithographic masks for manufacturing microcircuits.

series of cavities in the surface of the plate. The areas of the plate affected by the laser beam would be below the level of the untreated areas, which would be the ones printed.

The process could be carried out in practice by rotating the plate on a drum and making the laser beam scan it horizontally. The computer would control the speed at which the plate rotated and the rate at which the laser scanned. It would also fire laser pulses at the appropriate instants and control the intensity of the laser beam so that the depth and volume of the craters could be varied as required. The information needed by the computer would be obtained from magnetic tape or by scanning the photograph to be printed, or control could be exercised from a distant point over microwave radio circuits or land lines.

The 65-line screen plate commonly used in making newspaper halftone plates has about 655 dots to the square centimeter. Walter T. Reid of the Battelle Memorial Institute, Columbus, Ohio, has pointed out that a typical printing plate, which is approximately 20 cm. × 25 cm., would require 338,000 laser pulses to etch the entire surface. If one assumes that the laser can be pulsed at the high but not impossible rate of 50,000 times a second, such a plate could be etched in just under 7 seconds.

Even the best present-day electronic etching systems take about half an hour to do the same job.

The fact that the energy from a laser beam can be controlled and located much more precisely than an arc or a flame makes it very useful for high-precision welding. The laser is attractive in this application also because the rate at which energy is delivered to the joint is very high, so the weld is completed very quickly and little heat is lost by conduction through the metals being welded. But the laser has a very serious competitor in this field—the electron beam. This is an intense high-velocity beam formed when the electrons given off by a hot metal cathode are focused and accelerated by a series of electrodes. It is much easier to position electron beams accurately and to make them scan an area than it is to do these things with laser beams, but they can be used only in a vacuum because molecules of air scatter electrons out of the beam. Thus laser beams are better in conditions where a vacuum would be difficult or expensive to produce. One feature that has emerged from a thorough and clear analysis of the problem carried out a few years ago is that copper, silver, and gold are especially suited to laser welding because they are capable of withstanding the very high instan-

Left: laser beams can make welds through glass. Here a 0.005-cm-thick tantalum sleeve is welded to a molybdenum base in an inert argon atmosphere.

Opposite: a high-powered ruby laser pierces a hole in a steel sheet.

taneous temperatures associated with laser pulses without metal being expelled from the surface, and their high thermal conductivities mean that short-duration pulses can heat them quickly and effectively.

Processing Information

We saw in Chapter 3 how laser beams can carry information. In this section we shall describe how they can be used in a variety of ways to process information—information that is usually (though not always) in digital form.

Large-capacity memories in computers are frequently of the photographic type and the laser beam may prove very useful as a device for reading information out and writing it in. The kind of information used in conventional data-processing techniques is stored in digital form, as a pattern of dots. Writing information in means using a beam of light to produce a particular pattern of dots. Reading it out means scanning the film to detect which parts block the beam and which allow it through, so that the computer can recognize the pattern. Ordinary light sources can be used but lasers score in the intensity and smallness of their beams. Here again the laser beam has to compete with the electron beam, which can be made to scan much more easily but suffers from the great inconvenience that it has to be used in a vacuum.

One difficulty with present-day photographic memories is that they are nonreversible. The information is recorded on them in permanent form by conventional photographic techniques and can be changed only by manually removing the photographic plate and replacing it with another. Substantial research efforts are being directed toward making reversible photographic memories for use with lasers. Photochromic glasses, described on page 112, are one possibility, and others being investigated are thermoplastic and magnetooptic materials.

The Olivetti-General Electric Company of Milan has been investigating a magnetooptic variable memory, which makes use of the fact that one of the characteristics of a particular magnetic substance changes sharply with temperature in the neighborhood of one particular value known as the *compensation temperature*. F. Forlani and N. Minnaga suggested that a laser beam could act as an external source of heat. The computer memory would consist of a large number of pellets of the magnetic substance—gadolinium iron garnet—that could be scanned as required by the laser beam. The magnetic characteristic concerned is the *coercivity*, which has a value of about 230 oersteds at a temperature of 13°c. A change of only three degrees changes this value by as much as 75 per cent. A laser beam of fairly high intensity in the ultraviolet part of the spectrum would be needed to write in information. Reading the information out could be done with another laser beam, this time of low intensity, or possibly even with a beam of incoherent light. A pellet of gadolinium iron garnet affects the plane of polarization of light passing through it by an amount depending on its coercivity, and this change in polarization could be detected and interpreted on the far side. It is possible, at least in principle, to reach a very high storage density in this type of memory.

A particularly exciting possibility is the storage of information in holographic form. As explained on page 108, far more information can be stored in a given area by this means than by conventional magnetic computer memories, and the information is less likely to be lost irrecoverably as a result of scratches on the

A new semiconductor device for switching large blocks of electric power. Conventional solid-state switches are fired by pulses of electricity; this switch is fired by a pulse of infrared radiation from a gallium arsenide laser.

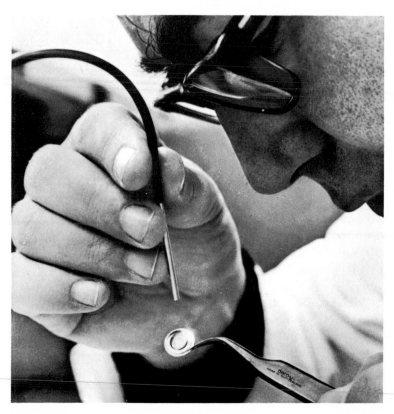

A synthetic-aperture radar image of the area around Monroe, Michigan. The image was obtained by optical processing techniques similar to those described in the text, and in the illustrations on pages 172-3, but instead of an array of several hundred dipoles, a single moving dipole carried in an aircraft was used. All the information collected as it traveled was processed.

microfilm. The three-dimensional nature of the stored information could also have important advantages. Indeed, it has been suggested that the human brain may store information in this way. It has always been a great puzzle how the vast amount of information stored in the human memory can be contained in the volume of the brain, and the holographic method might well be the way it is done.

Lasers also make novel forms of input and output computer displays possible. There is increasing demand for the storage and manipulation of pictorial and graphic data, three-dimensional as well as two-dimensional, in computers. An example quoted by William V. Smith of IBM's Thomas J. Watson Research Center, New York, is the production of a new automobile. Design engineers frequently wish to sketch changes in the style, and if they could view the automobile in the changed version from

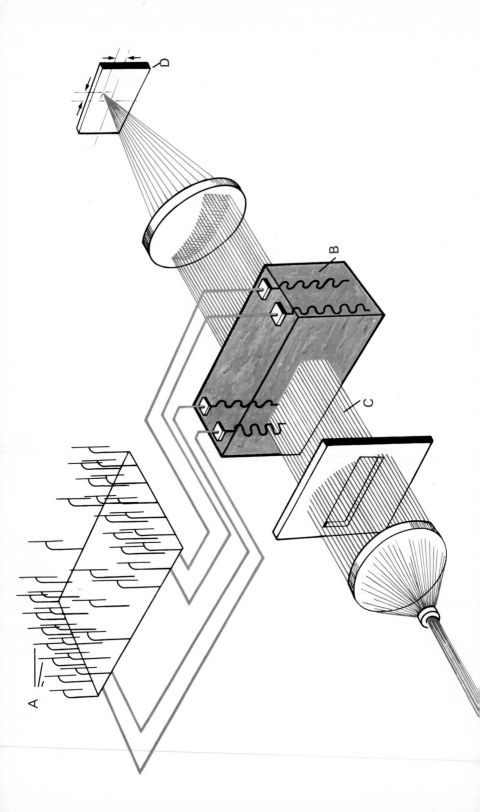

Opposite: an electrooptical processor for phased array antennas. Signals from the antennas (A) are converted by transducers into ultrasonic waves in a tank of water (B). These produce changes in refractive index that "process" the laser beam (C), which then passes through an integrating lens onto the screen (D). The photograph above shows the water tank and transducer leads.

several different angles the task would be greatly speeded up. The three-dimensional picture of the automobile would obviously be produced by holography, and the computer could alter it almost instantaneously in response to changes printed into it by the designers, so that a continuous feedback of information between designers and computer could take place.

A specialized field in which the laser is likely to find application almost immediately is the processing of various forms of radar signal. Long-range radar systems, of the type used in radio astronomy for making measurement on planets and the type used to detect intercontinental ballistic missiles, have to be exceptionally sensitive. In one particular experiment—the measurement of the length of the Venus day—the echoes returning from the planet are weaker than the background noise and cannot be distinguished from it by conventional techniques.

One way to recover the echoes is to give the outgoing radar pulse some very distinctive amplitude and frequency variations. The returning echoes can then be separated from the noise by checking their characteristics against those of the emitted pulse.

This can be done electronically, but the circuits are very complex. A laser system is much simpler. The returning signals and noise are amplified and converted into an acoustic signal that is passed through a tank full of liquid. The acoustic signal alters the refractive index of the liquid in a manner corresponding exactly to the variations of the signal and noise. A laser beam is passed through a reference photographic film containing a replica of the outgoing radar pulse and then through the tank. When the moving echo signal and the fixed replica are in line, a maximum of intensity is observed in the light on the far side of the tank, which is collected by a suitable optical system and detector. The photograph on page 171 shows a synthetic aperture radar image of the area around Monroe, Michigan, obtained by laser optical processing techniques.

A more sophisticated system based on the same idea, which was described by Moses Arm and several other scientists from Columbia University at a NATO symposium in Paris in 1965, provides a means of processing the signals received on the very complex *phased array radar aerials* coming into use for detecting ballistic missiles and satellites. These aerials are made up of vast numbers of individual aerial elements laid out in rows. Each one picks up signals from all directions, so it would be impossible to tell, with only one aerial, which direction the signal was coming from. But with an array there are slight differences in timing between the signals received by different elements, and hence there are phase differences between the outputs of the various aerials. Electronic circuits bring these outputs together and make them interfere with each other, with the result that the array responds only to signals from a particular direction specified to within several minutes of an arc. To make the array "look" in another direction it does not have to be physically swung around; it is only necessary to alter the characteristics of the circuits connected to the aerials.

The more elements there are in an array of this kind, the more accurately the direction can be pinpointed, and in recent years scientists have been talking in terms of several thousands of elements. But the amount of information received would then be so enormous as to make it prohibitively expensive, if not technically impossible, to process it with electronic circuits. Hence the interest in optical processors. In the experiments at Columbia University the array has 24 rows, each of 24 elements —that is, 576 elements in all. This is well below the limit that could be handled by an optical system, but it was chosen as a convenient number to allow the problems of optical processing to be investigated.

The method is illustrated on page 172. The primary source of light is a helium-neon gas laser emitting a wavelength of 6328 A. The most important part of the process is impressing the information from the aerial elements onto the laser beam. This is done by converting the electrical signals from all the 576 elements into ultrasonic waves that travel from top to bottom of a water-filled tank so that the space between the top and bottom of the tank is completely filled with the signals. The waves in the tank produce regions of compression and rarefaction of the water, altering its optical properties in subtle ways. The laser beam emerging from the far side of the tank is thereby modified in amplitude and phase and thus contains all the information about the time of arrival of the radar signal at each element in the array.

An integrating lens brings all the light in the laser beam onto a small area of the output plate. Interference occurs between the light waves that have passed through different parts of the modulator (the water tank) and the result is a spot of light whose position relative to the axis on the output plate gives the direction of arrival of the signal. A great advantage of the optical processor is that all possible aerial beams can exist at the same moment. Thus if in the case shown on page 172 there had also been a target on, say, the central "bore-sight" line of the array, this too would have been shown, as would any other targets within its view. A "wide-eyed view" like this is quite unlike the view obtained with an array using electronic data processing, which can look in only one direction at a time.

Lasers in Fundamental Research

Lasers are expected to be important as research tools in two ways—to study how light interacts with matter, and to teach us more about the nature of light itself. To end this book, we shall

Second harmonic generation. Above: a crystal of ammonium dihydrogen phosphate doubles the frequency of a ruby-laser beam, converting it from red to ultraviolet, which appears on the film as blue. Below: green light generated by an infrared beam striking a crystal of lithium niobate.

Opposite: a difference frequency, obtained when two laser beams are mixed in a crystal, is displayed on a cathode-ray screen attached to a spectrum analyzer.

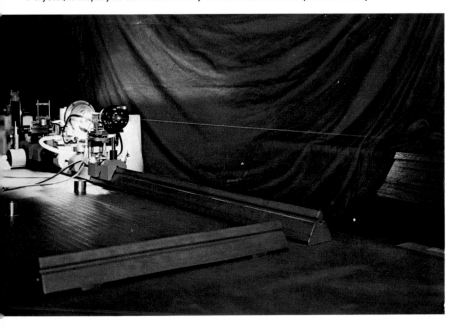

describe a few experiments that have been carried out with lasers and some of the many more that have been suggested.

A laser-beam intensity of 1000 million watts per square centimeter corresponds to an electric field of nearly a million volts per centimeter. If such a beam is focused by a lens to a spot 1 thousandth of a centimeter across, the beam intensity increases to a million billion (10^{15}) watts per square centimeter, which corresponds to an electric field-strength of a billion volts per centimeter. This enormous field-strength is comparable to the values of the electric fields within the atom itself, the fields that hold the electrons to the nucleus; and the laser should therefore help us learn a lot more about atomic energy levels and binding forces. We have already seen one practical consequence of such enormous fields, in the photograph on page 160. The disruption of air shown in that photograph is caused by the laser beam tearing the outermost electrons away from the air molecules. This ionization can occur in solids as well as in gases and a laser beam focused onto a small solid target generates a very dense miniature plasma. Indeed, it is largely the interest of plasma physicists that is encouraging the development of very powerful single-pulse laser systems such as the one developed by the Compagnie Générale d'Electricité (see page 54).

Another result of producing intensities as high as this is the generation of *harmonics*, familiar to us from the world of sound in general and music in particular. A loud sound wave impinging on an object can make the object generate waves with frequencies that are multiples of the original frequency. A sound wave whose frequency is 1000 cps., for example, can produce 2nd, 3rd, 4th, 5th . . . etc., harmonics on frequencies of 2000, 3000, 4000, 5000 ...etc., cps. An object of this kind is said to have a *nonlinear* response.

The enormous intensities of laser beams make it possible to observe nonlinear effects with light too, and here there is more than just a quantitative difference from ordinary light. The response to small disturbances in most physical systems follows a linear law: doubling the disturbance doubles the effect. If an ordinary beam of light shines onto certain types of crystal, some of the light is reflected and some goes straight through. If the intensity of the beam is doubled, the only result will be a doubling of the intensities of the reflected and transmitted beams. But if the intensity is increased many millions of times, rather than just two or three times, quite new effects—such as the generation of harmonics—begin to be observed. This kind of nonlinear response to light waves occurs because the dielectric constant of a material, which is a measure of its insulating ability, is not really a constant at all. At the very high field-strengths encountered in focused laser beams it depends on the value of the electric field intensity. The material will therefore distort any laser beam passing through it, and when analyzed this distortion is found to be the result of the addition of one or more harmonics to the original laser beam.

The first people to produce laser harmonics were Peter A. Franken, A. E. Hill, C. W. Peters, and G. Weinrech of the University of Michigan. They focused the 6943 A. beam from a ruby laser onto a block of quartz. On the far side of the block they were able to detect the original beam plus its second harmonic, a blue beam of wavelength 3472-A. (since wavelength is inversely proportional to frequency, this corresponds to a doubling of frequency). The intensity of the harmonic was only about 1 millionth of the intensity of the original beam in this first experiment but, later on, harmonics were produced containing as much as 20 per cent of the original beam.

A particularly fascinating experiment, shown in the lower photograph on page 177, is the one in which the original laser beam is in the near infrared part of the spectrum and is therefore invisible. The second harmonic of such a beam falls within the visible part of the spectrum, so that an onlooker will see the second harmonic as a beam of blue or green light that apparently originates in the middle of the crystal.

Another interesting process occurring when beams of high intensity are used is the *two-photon process*. We saw in Chapter 1 that the energy of a photon is proportional to its frequency, and that a photon can usually be absorbed by an atom only if its frequency corresponds to the energy difference between two levels of the atom; otherwise it will simply be scattered. In 1962 Abella, at Columbia University, observed an exception to this rule. He directed the 6943-A. beam of a ruby laser into the vapor of atomic cesium. This wavelength does not correspond to any of the energy differences of cesium, and would not normally be absorbed. There is, however, an energy-level difference corresponding almost exactly to that of two wave packets of the ruby-laser beam. If there happen to be two wave packets in the vicinity of an atom at the same time, the atom will absorb them both and be raised to its higher excited state. It then returns to the ground state via an intermediate energy level, emitting a photon of wavelength 5850 A. With ordinary light beams the probability that two photons will be close to the same atom at the same time is negligibly small, but this is no longer so with laser beams.

A closely related effect is the production of "sum" and "difference" frequencies when two laser beams of unequal frequencies are mixed. This is another phenomenon familiar in acoustics. Two tuning forks vibrating at frequencies differing by, say, 3 cps., produce a sound that alternately increases and diminishes in loudness at exactly this frequency. This *optical beating* had already been observed with noncoherent light in the mid-1950s, but it is far easier to obtain with lasers. Two lasers of different kinds, operating at widely spaced wavelengths, can be used; or the lasers can be of the same kind but operating at different temperatures. The difference frequency can be displayed on a cathode-ray tube, as in the photograph on page 176.

In 1966, D. C. Hanna, W. A. Gambling, and R. C. Smith of Southampton University, England, devised an ingenious mixing technique using two ruby lasers. We saw in Chapter 1 that ruby has two sharp fluorescent emission lines in the red part of the spectrum, known as the R_2 line and the R_1 line, with wavelengths of 6929 A. and 6943 A. Laser action normally occurs only on the R_1 line, but a ruby laser can be induced to operate on the R_2 line by inserting in the optical path a filter that passes the R_2 wavelength but rejects the R_1 wavelength. Hanna and his colleagues used two ruby crystals contained in the same optical

A laser reveals an art forgery at the Boston Museum. The paint on a supposedly 16th-century portrait was tested by a laser beam. The resulting spectrogram revealed the presence of zinc, which was not used in pigments until 1820.

cavity. One ruby provided the normal R_1 laser beam, the other ruby had the optical filter and provided the R_2 beam. The temperature of either ruby could be varied independently of the other, and in this way the two wavelengths could be varied over quite a wide range. Nonlinear mixing of the R_1 and R_2 beams resulted in a "difference" beam that could be tuned from 0.3 to 1 mm. in wavelength.

Nonlinear mixing is important because it gives us a way of producing coherent radiation on wavelengths that cannot be generated by direct laser action or by conventional microwave radio techniques, and it is helping to bridge the gap between the upper frequency limit of conventional microwave sources and the lowest frequency that can be generated by a laser.

A particularly interesting nonlinear phenomenon was observed almost accidentally by E. J. Woodbury of the Hughes Aircraft Company, in connection with the *Raman effect*. When light of a particular wavelength passes through a transparent substance, some of it is scattered. It has been known since 1928 that the scattered light contains not just the frequency of the original beam but also others differing from it by amounts related to the energy levels of the scattering molecules. Woodbury, in an experiment like that shown on page 184, passed the beam from a giant-pulse laser through nitrobenzene and found that the outgoing radiation contained frequencies slightly to the red side of the ruby-laser frequency, and differing from it by amounts equal to the vibrational frequencies of the nitrobenzene molecule. These laser Raman lines are not only much more intense than the conventional Raman lines; they are also coherent, so that the laser Raman effect, like second-harmonic generation, makes possible the generation of coherent light at new frequencies. It also gives scientists a quick way of getting information about the frequencies of molecular vibrations.

But the most exciting possibility offered by the laser to the theoretical physicist is probably checking the predictions of the quantum theory in the field of electrodynamics—the study of how electric currents interact with magnets or with other currents. All conventional experiments have borne out these predictions accurately but they were restricted to linear effects.

One of the nonlinear effects that can be tested is the generation of harmonics by free electrons when a laser beam strikes them. The use of free electrons has the great advantage that the predictions of the theory can be calculated precisely because the mathematician does not have to take into account the complications due to nearby atomic or molecular structures. Fiocco and Thompson of MIT hope to verify the theory by observing the scattering of a laser beam by a beam of electrons. The experiment is illustrated on page 186. A ruby-laser beam strikes a beam of electrons at right angles and photons bounce off the electrons. The chances of any given wave packet being scattered are extremely small and so far Fiocco and Thompson have reported that even with an electron-beam density of 5×10^9 electrons per cubic centimeter only one part in 10^{18} of the laser's light output reached the detector. With conventional light it would be impossible even to observe this tiny fraction, let alone to detect the harmonics in it.

Early experimenters with continuous-wave gas lasers were surprised to find that surfaces that appeared in ordinary light to be evenly illuminated took on a pattern of bright spots on a dark background when illuminated with laser light. Furthermore the appearance of a surface was different for observers in different positions and, when photographed, its appearance depended upon the aperture of the camera. None of this would be the case if the surface were perfectly smooth; but all surfaces have some degree of roughness, and the different parts of a rough surface reflect light to different degrees.

This granulation effect can be observed with ordinary light, but it is far less marked, and very exacting experimental conditions are required to observe it. This is because the brightness of each element of a surface depends on both the direction and the wavelength of the light that is hitting it. An element that scatters blue light in the direction of the observer may not reflect red light in that particular direction at all. Conventional light always contains quite a wide range of directions and wavelengths, however, so some light gets scattered in all directions and the granulation effect is masked. It is the directionality and narrow bandwidth, and also the intensity, of the laser beam that make it so good for

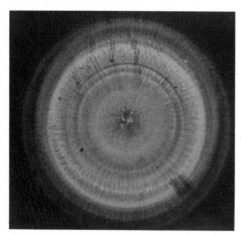

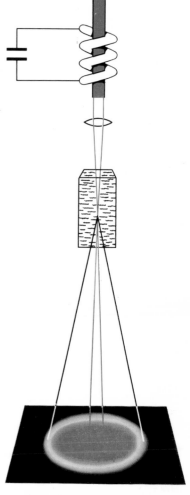

The laser Raman effect. A laser beam passes through a benzene-filled cell (right). The outgoing radiation contains new frequencies related to the vibrational frequencies of the benzene molecule, which are recorded on the film (above). The output also contains infrared radiation, which does not show up on the film.

Below: producing a difference frequency. Two ruby-laser beams of slightly different frequencies (red) are mixed in the crystal (yellow). The output is a beam whose wavelength is nearly a millimeter.

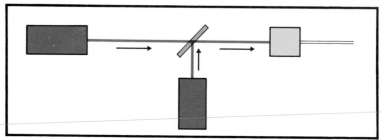

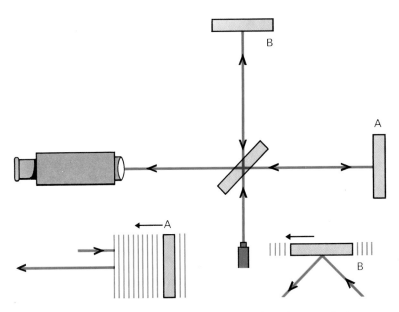

The Michelson-Morley experiment. The top diagram shows it as seen in the laboratory frame of reference. The lower diagrams show the motion of mirrors A and B, and the paths of the light beams reflected from them, relative to the ether.

observing these granulations.

The last laser experiment we shall describe is one successfully carried out by Ali Javan, T. S. Jaseja, and C. H. Townes to confirm the basic hypothesis of the special theory of relativity. This experiment was first performed in 1881 by A. A. Michelson and E. W. Morley in the way shown in the diagram above. At that time it was believed that light waves must travel through some kind of medium, just as sound waves travel through air. Sound cannot travel across a vacuum but light can, so physicists were forced to postulate the existence of a medium they called the *ether*, which had no mass or other detectable properties apart from the fact that it could support electromagnetic waves. It was assumed, of course, that the ether pervaded the whole of space, including what we think of as a complete vacuum.

If somebody is traveling very quickly away from a source of sound waves, the sound has to catch him up, and the speed with which a particular wave front passes him is less than the true velocity of sound. The same kind of effect—an apparent change

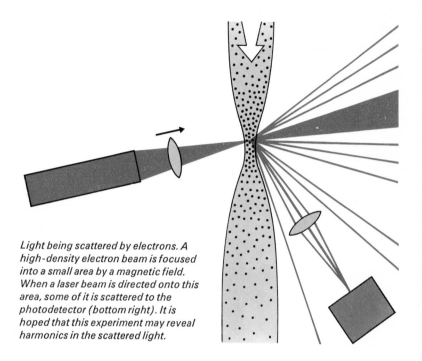

Light being scattered by electrons. A high-density electron beam is focused into a small area by a magnetic field. When a laser beam is directed onto this area, some of it is scattered to the photodetector (bottom right). It is hoped that this experiment may reveal harmonics in the scattered light.

in the velocity of light—should be observed by someone moving through the ether, and Michelson and Morley were trying to observe it. In fact they found that the velocity of light was not affected by any such motion, and this failure formed the starting point of Einstein's theory. The Michelson-Morley experiment is of fundamental importance to the theory of relativity and has often been repeated as more accurate methods became available.

The sought-after effect would be extremely small, and great refinement of experimental skill is needed for its detection. The apparatus of Michelson and Morley would have been able to detect a change in the velocity of light as small as 150 mm. per second. Later experiments improved this accuracy to about 15 mm. per second. Javan and his colleagues have achieved accuracies of 3 mm. per second with a laser system, and hope that the apparatus may ultimately be sensitive enough to detect a change in velocity as small as 0.03 mm. per second.

Their method was, in principle, very simple. Like Michelson and Morley they used the motion of the earth to supply the velocity through the hypothetical ether, and they simply placed their laser—a helium-neon gas laser—at various angles to the direction

A double-barreled laser used in meteorology. Working on the same principle as radar, it can detect and analyze clouds, dust particles, turbulence, and invisible atmospheric layers.

of this motion. Any change in the velocity of light would mean a difference in the time taken by the beam to travel from one of the laser mirrors to the other and back again, and this in turn would show up as a change in the frequency of the output beam.

These experiments are being performed in a wine cellar at Cape Cod. In a location like this, far removed from traffic and other mechanical disturbances, and on a day when the earth is quiet and the weather calm, the frequency of a laser beam remains constant within a few thousand cycles out of 10^{14}. Provided the laser structure is extremely rigid, the drift in frequency between two lasers can be kept down to as little as one part in 10^{13} per second, which implies that the length does not change by more than 10^{-13} meters, or a thousandth of the diameter of an atom. Even apparatus as sensitive as this has not revealed any change in the velocity of light to disturb the foundations of the theory of relativity.

Suggested Reading

G. Birnbaum, *Optical Masers*, Academic Press Inc., (London and New York, 1964)
R. Brown, Lasers: *A Survey of their Principles and Applications*,
Business Publications Ltd., (London, 1968)
C. C. Eaglesfield, *Laser Light: Fundamentals and Optical Communication*,
St. Martin's Press Inc., (New York, 1967) Macmillan & Co., Ltd., (London, 1967)
D. Fishlock (ed.), *A Guide to the Laser*, Macdonald & Co., Ltd., (London, 1967)
G. R. Fowles, *Introduction to Modern Optics*, Holt, Rinehart & Winston, Inc.,
(New York, 1968)
C. G. B. Garrett, *Gas Lasers*, McGraw Hill Publishing Company (London and New York, 1967)
O. S. Heavens, *Optical Masers*, Methuen & Co. Ltd., (London and New York, 1964)
A. Lempicki & H. Samelson, *Liquid Lasers*, (*Scientific American*, June 1967)
W. H. Freeman and Company, (San Francisco)
B. A. Lengyel, *Lasers*, John Wiley & Sons Inc., (London and New York, 1962)
P. E. McGuff, *Surgical Applications of the Laser*
G. C. Pimentel, *Chemical Lasers*, (*Scientific American*, April 1966) W. H. Freeman and Company, (San Francisco)
G. W. Stroke, *An Introduction to Coherent Optics and Holography*, Academic Press Inc., (London and New York, 1966)

Index

Note: Numbers in italics refer to illustrations and captions to illustrations.